The
LITTLE
BLACK
BOOK
of
METAL
HITS

Published by
Wise Publications
14-15 Berners Street, London, W1T 3LJ, England.
Exclusive distributors:
Music Sales Limited
Distribution Centre,
Newmarket Road, Bury St Edmunds, Suffolk, IP33 3YB, England.
Music Sales Pty Limited
120 Rothschild Avenue, Rosebery, NSW 2018, Australia.

Order No. AM985820
ISBN 1-84609-580-8

Cover designed by Michael Bell Design.
Project Editor: Tom Farncombe.
Printed in China.

www.musicsales.com

Wise Publications
part of The Music Sales Group
London / New York / Paris / Sydney / Copenhagen / Berlin / Madrid / Tokyo

All My Life

Words & Music by
Dave Grohl, Taylor Hawkins, Nate Mendel & Chris Shiflett

Intro | G5 | G5 | G5 | G5 |

| G5 | G5 | G5 | G5   ‖

Verse 1

G5
All my life I've been searching for something,

Something never comes never leads to nothing,

Nothing satisfies but I'm getting close,

Closer to the prize at the end of the rope.

All night long I dream of the day

When it comes around then it's taken away,

Leaves me with the feeling that I feel the most,

Feel it come to life when I see your ghost.

Link 1   ‖: Gm | Gm   Am |

| Gm | Gm   B♭m :‖

Verse 2

G5   A5
Calm down don't you resist,
G5   B♭5
   You have such a delicate wrist
G5   A5
   And if I give it a twist
G5   B♭5
Something to hold when I lose my grip
G5   A5
Will I find something in that?

cont.

G5   **B♭5**
  To give me just what I need

G5   **A5**
  Another reason to bleed

G5
One by one hidden up my sleeve

G5
One by one hidden up my sleeve.

E♭/G
Chorus 1 Hey don't let it go to waste

G5
 I love it but I hate the taste

C/E **F**   **B♭**
Weight keep pinning me down.

E♭/G
Hey don't let it go to waste

G5
 I love it but I hate the taste

C/E **F**   **B♭**
Weight keep pinning me down.

Link 2 | **Gm** | **Gm** **Am** |

     | **Gm** | **Gm** **B♭m** ‖

G5   **A5**
Verse 3 Will I find a believer?

G5   **B♭5**
 Another one who believes,

G5   **A5**
 Another one to deceive,

G5   **B♭5**
Over and over down on my knees.

G5   **A5**
If I get any closer,

G5   **B♭5**
 And if you open up wide,

G5   **A5**
 And if you let me inside,

G5
On and on I got nothing to hide,

On and on I got nothing to hide.

5

	E♭/G
Chorus 2	Hey don't let it go to waste
	G5
	I love it but I hate the taste
	C/E **F** **B♭**
	Weight keep pinning me down.

E♭/G
Hey don't let it go to waste

G5
   I love it but I hate the taste

C/E   **F**   **B♭**
Weight keep pinning me down.

Link 3

Gm		Gm	Am
Gm		Gm	B♭m

| G5 | G5 | G5 | G5 |
| G5 | G5 | G5 | G5 |

Verse 4   As Verse 1

G5
Bridge 1   And I'm done, done, onto the next one,

Done, done, and I'm onto the next one,

Done, done, and I'm onto the next one.

Done, done, and I'm onto the next one.

Done, done, and I'm onto the next one.

Done, done, and I'm onto the next one.

Done, done, and I'm onto the next one.

Done I'm done, and I'm onto the next.

Link 4

| G⁵ | G⁵ | G⁵ | G⁵ |

| G⁵ | G⁵ | G⁵ | G⁵ ‖

Bridge 2

G⁵
Done, done, onto the next one,

Done I'm done and I'm onto the next one

Done, done, onto the next one,

Done I'm done and I'm onto the next.

Chorus 3

E♭/G
Hey don't let it go to waste
G⁵
  I love it but I hate the taste
C/E   **F**   **B♭**
Weight keep pinning me down.
E♭/G
Hey don't let it go to waste
G⁵
  I love it but I hate the taste
C/E   **F**   **B♭**
Weight keep pinning me down.

Link 5

| G⁵ | G⁵ | G⁵ | G⁵ ‖

Outro

G⁵
Done, done and onto the next one

Done I'm done and I'm onto the next.

Am I Evil?

Words & Music by
Brian Tatler & Sean Lindon Harris

Intro
| E5 | E5 | E5 | E5 |

‖: E5 | E5 B5 | B♭5 | B♭5 F5 :‖ *Play 4 times*

| E5 | E5 D5 | E5 | E5 D5 |

| E5 | E5 D5 ‖

(Half time feel) | E5 B5 B♭5 F5 | E5 B5 B♭5 F5 | E5 F5 G5 | N.C. guitar fill ‖

riff A _____

‖: E5 G5 E5 | A5 E5 B♭5 A5 | E5 G5 E5 | A5 E5 B♭5 A5 :‖
Play 4 times

Verse 1

riff A
My mother was a witch, she was burned alive,

riff A
Thankless little bitch, for the tears I cried.

riff A
Take her down now, don't want to see her face,

riff A
All blistered and burnt, can't hide my disgrace.

riff B _____

| B5 D5 B5 | E5 B5 F5 E5 | B5 D5 B5 | E5 B5 F5 E5 ‖

Pre-chorus 1

riff B
Twenty-seven, everyone was nice,

Gotta see 'em make 'em pay the price.

riff B
See their bodies out on the ice,

Take my time.

| **Chorus 1** | | **riff A**   ‖

Chorus 1
| **riff A** ‖
Am I evil? yes, I am.
| **riff A** ‖
Am I evil? I am man, yes, I am.

Link 1   ‖: **riff A** :‖

Verse 2
| **riff A**   ‖
As I watched my mother die, I lost my head,
| **riff A**   ‖
Revenge now I sought, to break with my bread.
| **riff A** ‖
Taking no chances, you come with me,
| **riff A** ‖
I'll split you to the bone, help set you free.

Pre-chorus 2 As Pre-chorus 1

Chorus 2 As Chorus 1

Link 2

| E5 D5 | C5 | E5 G5 E5 | A5 E5 B♭5 A5| E5 D5 | C5
               Ooh.
| E5 D5 | C5 | E5 D5 | C5 | E5 D5 | C͡5 ‖

Link 3

(faster)
| A5 | A5 G5 D5 | A5 | A5 C5 G5 |

riff C _____
| A5 | A5 G5 D5 | A5 | A5 C5 G5 ‖

Verse 3

E5   D5 E5   D5
  On with the action now,   I'll strip your pride,
E5   D5 E5   D5
  I'll spread your blood around, I'll see you ride.
E5   D5 E5   D5
  Your face is scarred with steel, wounds deep and neat,
E5   D5 E5   D5
  Like a double dozen before ya, smells so sweet.

Chorus 3

| **riff C**   ‖

Am I evil? yes, I am.

| **riff C**   ‖

Am I evil? I am man.

Verse 4

E5   D5   E5   D5

My soul is longing for,   await my heir,

E5   D5   E5   D5

Sent to avenge my mother,   sweep myself.

E5   D5   E5   D5

My face is long forgot,   my face not my own,

E5   D5   E5   D5

Sweet and timely whore,   take me home.

Chorus 4   As Chorus 3

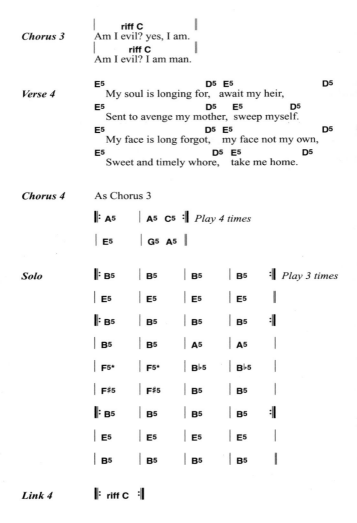

Link 4   ‖: riff C :‖

10

Verse 5	E5	D5 E5		D5
	On with the action now,		I'll strip your pride,	

Verse 5

E5   D5 E5   D5
On with the action now,   I'll strip your pride,

E5   D5 E5   D5
I'll spread your blood around,   I'll see you ride.

E5   D5 E5   D5
Your face is scarred with steel,   your spirit ends,

E5   D5 E5   D5
Like a double dozen before ya, no romance.

Chorus 5

| **riff C**   ‖
Am I evil? yes, I am.
| **riff C**   ‖
Am I evil? I am man.
| **riff C**   ‖
Am I evil? yes, I am
| **riff C**   ‖ (E5)
Am I evil? I am man, (yeah.)

Outro

| E5 D5 | D5 | E5 D5 | D5 |
Yeah

| E5 D5 | D5 | E5 D5 | D5   ‖

‖: **riff A** :‖ *Play 4 times*

| G5 E5 ‖

Ain't Talkin' 'Bout Love

Words & Music by
Edward Van Halen, Alex Van Halen,
Michael Anthony & David Lee Roth

Intro   ‖: **Am** | **G** | **Am** | **G**   :‖ *x2*
Guitar riff

Verse 1
                    Am G   **Am G**
I heard the news baby,   all about your disease
                         Am   **G**
Yeah you may have all you want, baby,
                      Am G
But I got somethin' you need.

Chorus 1
                              Am G
Oh yeah, ain't talkin' 'bout love
                       Am G
My love is rotten to the core
                    Am G
Ain't talkin' 'bout love
                       Am G
Just like I told you be - fore, yeah before.

Verse 2
                              Am   G
You know you're semi-good lookin',
                        Am G
And on the streets again
                                Am
Oh yeah you think you're really cookin' baby,
G   **Am**
   You better find yourself a friend,
G
My friend.

Chorus 2

                     Am G
Ain't talkin' 'bout love

                       Am G
My love is rotten to the core

                     Am G
Ain't talkin' 'bout love

                   Am   **G**
Just like I told you before, uh be - fore, uh before, before.

Guitar solo 1 ‖: **Am** | **G** | **Am** | **G** :‖

Chorus 3

                     Am G
Ain't talkin' 'bout love

                       Am G
My love is rotten to the core

                     Am G
Ain't talkin' 'bout love

                   Am   **G**
Just like I told you be - fore, uh be - fore.

Verse 3

               Am   **G**   **Am G**
I been to the edge,   an' there I stood an' looked down

                   Am
You know I lost a lot of friends there baby,

G   **Am G**
  I got no time to mess around

                                Am   **G**
Mmmm, so if you want it got to bleed for it baby

                   Am   **G**
Yeah, got to got to bleed baby

                       Am   **G**
Mmmm, you got to got to bleed baby

                   Am   **G**
Hey, got to got to bleed baby.

Chorus 4

        Am G
Ain't talkin' 'bout love

            Am G
My love is rotten to the core

        Am G
Ain't talkin' 'bout love

          Am   **G**
Just like I told you be - fore, be - fore, before, (before).

Chorus 5

        Am G
Ain't talkin' 'bout love

          Am G
Don't wanna talk about love

          Am G
Don't need to talk about love

           Am   **G**
Ain't gonna talk about love, no more, no more, ah.

Guitar solo 2 ‖: **Am** | **G** | **Am** | **G**   :‖

Outro   **Am G**
‖: Hey, hey, hey   :‖ *Play 9 times*

     | **Am B** | **C** | **Am B** | **Em** |

     | **Am B** | **C** | **Am B** | **Em**   ‖

Animal

Words & Music by
Steve Clark, Phil Collen, Joe Elliott,
Robert John 'Mutt' Lange & Rick Savage

x2

Intro   ‖: B♭sus2 | Csus4 Dm7 | B♭sus2 | Csus4 Dm7 :‖

Verse 1

B♭add9 Csus4   Dm7 B♭add9
A wild ride,   over stony ground,

Csus4/G Dm7/A B♭add9 Csus4   Dm7   B♭add9
Such a lust for life,   the circus comes to town,

Csus4/G   Dm7/A B♭add9 Csus4   Dm7   B♭add9
We are the hungry ones,   on a lightning raid,

Csus4/G   Dm7/A B♭add9 Csus4   Dm7   B♭add9
Just like a river   runs,   like a fire needs flame

Csus4/G   Dm7/A
Oh   I burn for you.

Chorus 1

B   F♯   C♯
I gotta feel it in my blood,

Oh whoa.

B   F♯   C♯
I need your touch don't need your love,

Oh whoa.

F♯
And I want,

E6/9
And I need,

B
And I lust,

15

cont.

A⁶
Animal.

F♯
And I want,

E6/9
And I need,

B
And I lust,

A⁶ N.C.
Animal.

Verse 2
B♭add⁹ Csus⁴   Dm⁷   B♭add⁹
I cry wolf,   given mouth to mouth

Csus⁴/G Dm⁷/A B♭add⁹   Csus⁴   Dm⁷   B♭add⁹
  Like a movin' heartbeat   in the witching hour

Csus⁴/G   Dm⁷/A   B♭add⁹ Csus⁴   Dm⁷ B♭add⁹
  I'm runnin' with the wind,   a shadow in the dust,

Csus⁴/G   Dm⁷/A B♭add⁹
  And like the drivin' rain

**   Csus⁴/G Dm⁷/A B♭add⁹ Csus⁴/G**
Yeah,   like a restless rust

Dm⁷/A
I never sleep.

Chorus 2   As Chorus 1

A F G N.C. G   A F G
Huh!   Oh!   Cry wolf baby,

N.C. G
Cry tough

**   G   D   E**
Gonna hunt you like a,

**   E   G D E**
A, a - a - ni - mal

N.C.
Gonna take your love 'n' run.

Guitar Solo   ‖: **B♭** | **C   Dm⁷** :‖   *x4*

Chorus 3   As Chorus 1

Chorus 4

            F#
And I want,   (and I want)

           E6/9
And I need,   (and I need)

        B
And I lust,   (and I lust)

   A6
Animal,   (animal).

            F#
And I want (take me),

          E6/9
And I need (tame me),

        B
And I lust (make me your . . .)

          A6
Animal (. . . animal).

            F#
And I want (show me),

         E6/9
And I need (stroke me),

        B
And I lust (let me be your...)

          A6   **N.C.**
Animal,   (....animal).

            F#
And I want (I want),

         E6/9
And I need, (ooh ooh ooh)

        B
And I lust, (animal)

A6
Animal.

N.C.
Oh!

Heh, heh.

Balls To The Wall

Words & Music by
Peter Baltes, Wolf Hoffmann,
Udo Dirkschneider & Stefan Kaufmann

Intro

‖: G5 E5 E5 D5 E5 E5 E5 | G5 E5 E5 D5 E5 E5 E5 |

| 1, 3.

| G5 E5 E5 D5 E5 G5 | G5   G♯5 A5 G5 :‖

| 4.

| G5 | G5   G5   E5 ‖

Verse 1

D5   G D5
   Too many slaves in this world
E5   G E5
   Die by torture and pain
D5   G D5
   Too many people do not see
E5   G E5
   They're killing themselves – going insane
D5   G D5
   Too many people do not know
E5   G E5
   Bondage is over the human race
D5   G D5
   They believe slaves always lose
E5
   And this fear keeps them down.

Pre-chorus 1

B5   **G5**
Watch the damned   (God bless ya)

B5   **D/A**
They're gonna break their chains (hey)

      B5   **G5**
No, you can't stop them (God bless ya)

B5   **A5**
They're coming to get you

        N.C.
And then you'll get your...

Chorus 1

E5   **G5**   **F♯5** | **E5**   **G5** **D5** |
Balls to the wall, man

E5   **G5**   **F♯5** | **E5**   **G5** **D5** |
Balls to the wall

              E5   **G5** **F♯5** | **E5**   **G5** **D5** |
You'll get your balls to the wall, man

E5   **G5**   **D5**   **E5**   **G5 E5**
Balls to the wall – balls to the wall.

Verse 2

D5   **G D5**
You may screw their brains

E5   **G E5**
You may sacrifice them, too

D5   **G D5**
You may mortify their flesh

E5   **G E5**
You may rape them all

D5   **G D5**
One day the tortured stand up

E5   **G E5**
And revolt against the evil

D5   **G D5**
They make you drink your blood

E5
And tear yourself to pieces.

Pre-chorus 2   As Pre-chorus 1

Chorus 2

E5   **G5**   **F♯5** | **E5**   **G5** **D5** |
Balls to the wall, man

E5   **G5**   **F♯5** | **E5**   **G5** **D5** |
Balls to the wall

              E5   **G5** **F♯5** | **E5**   **G5** **D5** |
You'll get your balls to the wall, man

E5   **G5**   **D5**   **E5**
Balls to the wall – balls to the wall.

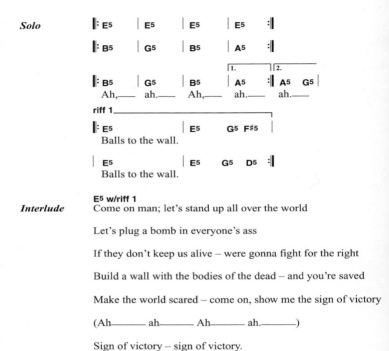

Solo

‖: E5 | E5 | E5 | E5 :‖

‖: B5 | G5 | B5 | A5 :‖

                                         1.   2.

‖: B5 | G5 | B5 | A5 :‖ A5 G5 |
  Ah,— ah.— Ah,— ah.— ah.—

riff 1 _____

‖: E5 | E5   G5 F♯5 |
  Balls to the wall.

| E5 | E5   G5 D5 :‖
  Balls to the wall.

Interlude

E5 w/riff 1
Come on man; let's stand up all over the world

Let's plug a bomb in everyone's ass

If they don't keep us alive – were gonna fight for the right

Build a wall with the bodies of the dead – and you're saved

Make the world scared – come on, show me the sign of victory

(Ah———— ah———— Ah———— ah.————)

Sign of victory – sign of victory.

Pre-chorus 3   As Pre-chorus 2

Chorus 3

   E5   G5   F♯5 | E5   G5   D5 |
‖: Balls to the wall, man
 E5   G5   F♯5 | E5   G5   D5
Balls to the wall.   You'll get your...
 E5   G5   F♯5 | E5   G5   D5 |
Balls to the wall, man
 E5   G5 | D5   :‖
Balls to the wall.   You'll get your
 E5   G5   N.C.
Balls to the wall, man.

Beyond The Realms Of Death

Words & Music by
Robert Halford & Leslie Binks

Intro ‖: Bm(add11) | Bm(add11)/A Gmaj13 | E5 F♯5 :‖

Verse 1

Bm(add11)   **Bm(add11)/A**
He had e - nough

Gmaj13   **E5**   **F♯5**
He couldn't take any - more——

Bm(add11)   **Bm(add11)/A**
He'd found a place

          Gmaj13   **E5**   **F♯5**
In his mind and slammed the door

Bm(add11)   **Bm(add11)/A**
No matter how they tried

          Gmaj13   **E5**   **F♯5**
They couldn't under - stand

Bm(add11)   **Bm(add11)/A**
They washed and dressed him

Gmaj13   **F♯5**
Fed him by hand.

Chorus 1

| **A5 B5 B5**   **A5 B5 B5** |
          Yeah!   I've left the

A5   **B5**   **B5**   **A5 B5 C♯5 D5 C♯5**
World be - hind

A5 B5 B5   **A5 B5 B5** | **A5 B5   B5**   **A5 B5 C♯5 D5 C♯5**
          I am   safe here   in my mind

          A5 B5 B5   **A5 B5 B5** |
I'm free to speak   with

A5 B5   B5   **A5 B5 C♯5 D5 C♯5** |
My own kind

                A5 B5 B5   **A5 B5 B5** |
This is my—— life, this is my—— life

A5 B5   B5   **A5 B5 C♯5 D5 C♯5 F♯5** |
I'll de - cide not you.

Verse 2

Bm(add11)   Bm(add11)/A
  Withdrawn he'd sit there

Gmaj13   E5   F#5
  Stare blank into space

Bm(add11)   Bm(add11)/A
  No sign of life——

       Gmaj13   E5   F#5
Would flicker on his face

Bm(add11)   Bm(add11)/A
  Until one day he smiled

   Gmaj13   E5   F#5
It seemed as though with pride

Bm(add11)   Bm(add11)/A
  The wind kissed him

Gmaj13   F#5
  Goodbye – and then he died.

Chorus 2   As Chorus 1

Bridge 1

F#5
Keep the world with all its sin

E5
It's not fit for livin' in

Chorus 3

| A5 B5 B5 | A5 B5 B5 | A5 B5 B5 |
   Yeah!   I   will   start a - gain

| A5 B5 B5 | A5 B5 B5 |
It can take for - ever, and ev - er, and ever

| A5 B5 B5 | A5 B5 C#5 D5 C#5 |
and ever, but I'll still win.

Solo

‖: B5 | A5 | G5 | [1-7.] E5 F#5 :‖ [8.] F#5 ‖

Link

| Bm(add11) | Bm(add11)/A | Gmaj13 | E5 F#5 ‖

Verse 2	**Bm(add11)** **Bm(add11)/A** How many like him
	Gmaj13 **E5** **F♯5** Are there still
	Bm(add11) **Bm(add11)/A** But to us, all
	Gmaj13 **E5** **F♯5** Seem to have lost the will
	Bm(add11) **Bm(add11)/A** They lie in thousands
	Gmaj13 **E5** **F♯5** Plagued and lost
	Bm(add11) **Bm(add11)/A** **E5** **F♯5** Is nothing worth this bitter cost?

Chorus 4	As Chorus 1

Bridge 2	As Bridge 1

Outro solo

‖: **A5 B5 B5**   **A5**   **B5 B5** |
(8°) Be - yond the realms of

⌐1-7.————————————————————
| **A5 B5 B5**   **A B5 C♯5 D5 C♯5** :‖

⌐8. rall.————————————————————
| **A5 B5 B5**   **A B5 C♯5 D5 C♯5 F♯5** | **F♯5** ‖
death.————

Bitch School

Words & Music by
David St. Hubbins, Derek Smalls & Nigel Tufnell

Intro   ‖: **A5** | **A5**   **D5** :‖ *Play 4 times*

Verse 1

A5
You been bad

   A5   **D5**
Don't do what I say,

     A5
You don't listen

       D5
And you never obey.

    A5
I try to teach you,

          D5
But you just won't be good

E
    You won't behave the way

A big girl should.

   F♯8
It's time to give that whip a crack

   G8   **F♯8 G8**   **F♯8**   **G8**   **F♯8 G8**   **F♯8**
I'm gon - na have to   send you back to

Chorus 1

A5   **D5**
Bitch school,
A5   **D5**
Bitch school.

Verse 2

         A5
You're a beauty.
                D5
You're the best of your breed.
        A5
You're a handful,
            D5
And I know what you need.
      A5
You need training,
           D5
Gonna bring you to heel,
E
  I'm gonna break you with my will of steel.
F#8
Discipline's my middle name,
    G8 F#8 G8 F#8   **G8** **F#8 G8**   **F#8**
And no one   comes back the same from

Chorus 2   As Chorus 1

Bridge

C5   **B♭5**   **F5**   **C5**   **B♭5**   **F5**
  No more sniffing strangers, or running free at night,
D5   **C5**   **G5** **D5**   **C5**   **G5**
  You think my bark's bad, honey - wait till you feel my bite.
E5   **D5** | **A5** | **A5 D5** | **A5** | **A5 D5** ‖
  Wait till you feel my bite.

Guitar solo   ‖: **A5** | **A5** **D5** :‖ *Play 2 times*

Verse 3

     A5
You got problems,

       D5
You whine and you beg.

     A5
When I'm busy

       D5
You wanna dance with my leg.

     A5
I'm gonna chain you,

       D5
Make you sleep out of doors

E
  And you're so fetching when you're down on all fours.

F♯8
  And when you hear your master

G8 **F♯8** **G8**   **F♯8** **G8** **F♯8** **G8**   **F♯8** **G8**   **F♯8**
You will come a   lit - tle fas - ter thanks to

Outro

A5   **D5**
Bitch school,

A5   **D5**
Bitch school,

A5   **D5**
Bitch school, gonna have to take you back to

A5   **D5**
Bitch school.

Black Hole Sun

Words & Music by
Chris Cornell

| *Intro* | | Asus⁴ | C⁶ᐟ⁹ | G⁵ | | F♯⁵ | | Fsus⁴ | E⁷ | | E⁷ | | |

Verse 1

  (E7)   **A⁶**   **C⁶**
In my eyes, indisposed,
       G⁵   **F♯m**
In disguise as no one knows,
        F   **Esus⁴**
Hide the face, lies the snake,
     A⁶   **A/G**   **B♭**
The sun in my disgrace.

Verse 2

         A⁶   **C⁶**
Boiling heat, summer stench,
          G⁵   **F♯m**
'Neath the black the sky looks dead.
        F   **Esus⁴**
Call my name through the cream
      A⁶   **A/G**   **B♭**
And I'll hear you scream again.

Chorus 1

N.C.   **Fsus⁴**   **E⁷**
Black hole sun won't you come
    A⁵   **A⁵/G**   **C**
And wash away the rain?
        Fsus⁴   **E⁷**
Black hole sun won't you come,
        D   **Dsus⁴**   **D**   **E⁵**
Won't you come?   Won't you come?

        A⁶   **C⁶**
Stuttering, cold and damp,

     G⁵   **F♯m**
Steal the warm wind, tired friend.

       F   **Esus⁴**
Times are gone for honest   men

        A⁶   **A/G**   **B♭**
And sometimes far too long for snakes.

Verse 4

       A⁶   **C⁶**
In my shoes, a walking sleep,

     G⁵   **F♯m**
And my youth I pray to keep.

       F   **Esus⁴**
Heaven send hell away,

       A⁶   **A/G**   **B♭**
No-one sings like you anymore.

Chorus 2

N.C.   **Fsus⁴**   **E⁷**
Black hole sun won't you come

     A⁵   **A⁵/G**   **C**
And wash away the rain?

       Fsus⁴   **E⁷**
Black hole sun won't you come,

      D **Dsus⁴ D** **C**
Won't you come?

       Fsus⁴   **E⁷**
Black hole sun won't you come

     A⁵   **A⁵/G**   **C**
And wash away the rain?

       Fsus⁴   **E⁷**
Black hole sun won't you come,

      D **Dsus⁴ D C E⁵**
Won't you come?_____

      D **Dsus⁴ D C E⁵**
Won't you come?_____

      D **Dsus⁴ D C E⁵**
Won't you come?_____

      D **Dsus⁴ D C E⁵**
Won't you come?_____

Instrumental ‖: E5 | Gadd#4 :‖ G5* A5 |

Link
         A6   C6
Hang my head, drown my fear
        G5   F#m
'Til you all just disappear.

Chorus 3
N.C.   Fsus4   E7
Black hole sun won't you come
     A5   A5/G   C
And wash away the rain?
        Fsus4   E7
Black hole sun won't you come,
         D Dsus4 D C
Won't you come?
        Fsus4   E7
Black hole sun won't you come
     A5   A5/G   C
And wash away the rain?
        Fsus4   E7
Black hole sun won't you come,
         D Dsus4 D C E5
Won't you come?_____
         D Dsus4 D C E5
Won't you come?_____
         D Dsus4 D C E5
Won't you come?_____
         D Dsus4 D C E5
Won't you come?_____
         D Dsus4 D C E5
Won't you come?_____
         D Dsus4 D C E5
Won't you come?_____
         D Dsus4 D C E5
Won't you come?_____
         D Dsus4 D C E5
Won't you come?_____

| E5 | Gadd#4 | G5*   A5   ‖

Burn The Witch

Words & Music by
Josh Homme, Joey Castillo & Troy Van Leeuwen

Intro ‖: **E5** | **E5** :‖ *Play 6 times*

E5
Verse 1 Holding hands, skipping like a stone.

On our way, to see what we have done.

The first to speak, is the first to lie.

The children cross their heats and hope to die.

B Em   B
Chorus 1 Bite your tongue,
Em   B   Em   B   Em
Swear to keep your mouth shut.

Interlude ‖: **E5** | **E5** | **E5** | **E5** :‖ *Play 8 times*

E5
Verse 2 Ask yourself, will I burn in Hell?

Then write it down, and cast it in the well.

There they are, the mob it cries for blood.

To twist the tale, into firewood.

Fan the flames, with a little lie.

Then turn your cheek, until the fire dies.

The skin it peels, like the truth, away.

What it was, I will never say. Ah, oh. Ah, oh.

	B **Em** **B** **Em**
Chorus 2	Bite your tongue, swear to keep,

B   **Em**
Keep your mouth shut.
B   **Em**
Make up something,
B   **Em**   **E5**
Make up something good.

Interlude 2	‖: **E5** :‖ *Play 5 times*
Guitar Solo	‖: **E5** :‖ *Play 16 times*

E5

Chorus 3   Holding hands, skipping like a stone.

Burn the witch, burn to ash and bone.

Burn the witch, burn to ash and bone.

Burn the witch, burn to ash and bone.

E5

Outro   ‖: Oh.   :‖   *Play 12 times*

Can I Play With Madness?

Words & Music by
Bruce Dickinson, Steve Harris & Adrian Smith

Intro

N.C.
Can I play with madness?

‖: **D**　　|**D/C**　**Csus²**|**G5**　　|**Dsus⁴**　**D**　**Dsus⁴**　**D**　**Dsus⁴** :‖

Verse 1

D　　　　　　　　　　**D/C**
Give me the sense to won-der,

　G　　　　　　　　　**Dsus⁴**　**D**　**Dsus⁴**　**D**　**Dsus⁴**
To wonder if I'm free.

D　　　　　　　　　　**Csus²**
Give me the sense to won-der,

　G　　　　　　　　　**Dsus⁴**　**D**　**Dsus⁴**　**D**　**Dsus⁴**
To know I can believe.

D　　　　　　　　　　**D/C**
Give me the strength to hold my head up,

G　　　　　　　　　　**Dsus⁴**　**D**　**Dsus⁴**　**D**　**Dsus⁴**
Spit back in their face.

D　　　　　　　　　**Csus²**
　　Don't need no key to un-lock this door,

G
Gotta break down the walls,

　　　D5　　　**A5**　**D5**　　　**A5**　**D5**　**A5**
Break out of this bad place.

Chorus

B5　　　　　**G5**
Can I play with madness?

　　　　D5　　　　　　　　　　**A5**　　　**B5**
The pro-phet stared at his crystal ball.

　　　　　G5
Can I play with madness?

　　Esus⁴　　　　　　**E**　　**B5**
There's no　　vision there at all.

　　　　　G5
Can I play with madness?

　　　　D5　　　　　　　　　　　　**A5**　　　　　**B5**
The pro-phet looked at me and laughed at me. Ha! He said,

　　　　　G5
Can I play with madness?

　　　　　　　D5　**A5**　　**D5**　**A5**　　**D5**　**A5**
He said, 'You're blind,　too blind　to see.'

Interlude ‖: **D** | **D/C** **Csus2** | **G5** | **Dsus4 D Dsus4 D Dsus4** :‖

Verse 2
D   **D/C**
I screamed aloud to the old man,
G
I said, 'Don't lie and say
                              Dsus4 D Dsus4 D Dsus4
You don't know.
D   **Csus2**
 I say you'll pay for this mischief, aw,
  G   **Dsus4 D Dsus4 D Dsus4**
In this world or the next.'
D   **D/C**
Oh, and then he fixed me with a freezing glance,
        G   **Dsus4 D Dsus4 D Dsus4**
And the hell fires raged in his eyes.
                        D
He said 'You wanna know the truth, son?
            Csus2   **G5**
Lord, I'll tell you the truth, your soul's
                              D5   **A5**   **D5**   **A5**
Gonna burn in the lake of fire'

Chorus 2   As Chorus 1

Interlude   **(E)**   **G5**   **(E)**   **G5**   **A5**
                   Aw,   lis-ten to me,   said the
                (E)   **G5**   **(E)**   **G5**   **A5**
                prophet.

                ‖: **(G)** | **B♭5** | **(G)** | **B♭5**   **C5**   :‖
Solo   ‖: **(E)** | **G5** | **(E)** | **G5**   **A5**   :‖

                                        x3
Interlude   ‖: **(G)**   :‖

                D5   **A5**   **D5**   **A5**   **D5**   **A5**

Chorus 3   As Chorus 1

                N.C.
                Can I play with madness?

33

Chop Suey!

Words by Serj Tankian & Daron Malakian
Music by Daron Malakian

Intro ‖: (Gm) | (Gm) | (Gm) | (Gm) :‖

‖: Gm | Cm/E♭ | Adim | E♭ :‖

‖: A♭5 G5 | B♭5 C5 :‖: G5 G♭5 | A5 C5 :‖

Verse 1

G5   N.C. G5   G♭5 N.C.
Wake up! Grab a brush and put a little (make-up),

G♭5   G5   N.C.
Hide the scars to fade away the (shake-up),

G5   G♭5 N.C.
Why'd you leave the keys upon the table?

G♭5   G5   N.C
Here you go create another fa - ble.

              G5   G♭5
You wanted to grab a brush and put a little make-up,

              G5
You wanted to hide the scars to fade away the shake-up,

You wanted to.

G5   G♭5
Why'd you leave the keys upon the table? You wanted to.

Chorus 1

G♭5   Gm
I don't think you trust

Cm/E♭ Adim E♭   Gm
In   my   self-righteous suicide.

Cm/E♭ Adim   E♭
I   cry when angels deserve to (die.)

| A♭5 G5 | B♭5 C5 | A♭5 G5 | B♭5 C5 | A♭5 ‖
die. _____

Verse 2   As Verse 1

Chorus 2

G♭5   Gm
I don't think you trust

Cm/E♭ Adim E♭   Gm
In   my   self-righteous suicide.

Cm/E♭ Adim   E♭   Gm
I   cry when angels deserve to die. _____

Chorus 3

Cm/E♭ Adim E♭   Gm
In   my   self-righteous suicide.

Cm/E♭ Adim   E♭
I   cry when angels deserve to die.

| A♭5 G5 | B♭5 C5 | A♭5 G5 | B♭5 C5 ||

Coda

A♭5   G5   B♭5   C5
Father, Father, Father, Father,

A♭5   G5   B♭5   C5
Father, Father, Father, Father,

G5   G♭5   A5   C5
Father into your hands   I commend my spirit.

G5   G♭5
   Father into your hands…

A5   C5   Gm
Why have you forsaken me?

E♭5   B♭5
In your eyes forsaken me?

E♭5   Gm
In your thoughts forsaken me?

E♭5   B♭5   E♭5
In your heart forsaken me?

Gm E♭5 B♭5 E♭5   Gm
Trust in   my self-righteous suicide.

E♭5 B♭5   E♭5   Gm
I   cry when angels deserve to die.

E♭5 B♭5 E♭5   Gm
In   my self-righteous suicide.

E♭5 B♭5   E♭5   Gm
I   cry when angels deserve to die.

Crawling

Words & Music by
Chester Bennington, Mike Shinoda, Rob Bourdon,
Joseph Hahn & Brad Delson

Intro

| C#m | C#m | Amaj7 | Amaj7 |

| Amaj7 | B | C#m | E ‖

Chorus 1

C#   A add9 E   B
Crawling in my skin, these wounds they will not heal.
C#   A add9 E   B
Fear is how I fall, confusing what is real. _____

Link

| C#m | Amaj7 | E | B ‖

Verse 1

C#m   Amaj7
  There's something inside me that pulls beneath the surface,
E   B
  Consuming, confusing,
C#m   Amaj7
  This lack of self-control I fear is never ending,
E   B   Amaj7   B
  Controlling, I can't seem _____ to find myself again,
              C#m
My walls are closing in,

(Without a sense of self confidence,
      E   Amaj7
I'm convinced that there's just too much pressure to take),
     B
I've felt this way before,
      C#m E
So insecure. _____

Chorus 2   As Chorus 1

Verse 2

C#m   Amaj⁷

Discomfort endlessly has pulled itself upon me,

E   B

Distracting,   reacting.

C#m   Amaj⁷

Against my will I stand beside my own reflection,

E   B   Amaj⁷

It's haunting how I can't seem _____

                  B

To find myself again,

                    C#m

My walls are closing in,

(Without a sense of confidence,

            E   Amaj⁷

I'm convinced that there's just too much pressure to take),

            B

I've felt this way before,

          C#m   E | E |

So insecure. _____

Chorus 3   As Chorus 1

Chorus 4

C#   A add9   E   B

Crawling in my skin, these wounds they will not heal.

C#   A add9   E   B   C#m

Fear is how I fall, confusing, confusing what is real. _____

Coda

                                        Amaj⁷

(There's something inside me that pulls beneath the surface,

E   B   C#m

Consuming), confusing what is real.

                          Amaj⁷   E

(This lack of self-control I fear is never ending, controlling),

          B

Confusing what is real.

Crazy Train

Words & Music by
Ozzy Osbourne, Bob Daisley & Randy Rhoads

Intro   All aboard ha ha ha ha——

| F#5 | A5 E5 | F#5 | D5 E5 |
| F#5 | A5 E5 | F#5 | D5 E5 |

(Guitar riff)

| F#5 | A5 E5 | F#5 | D5 E5 |
| F#5 | A5 E5 | F#5 | D5 E5 |

| A | Aadd9/11 A | A | Aadd9/11 A ‖

Verse 1

A   Aadd9/11   A   Aadd9/11 A
Crazy,   but that's how it goes

A   Aadd9/11 A   Aadd9/11 A
Millions of people   living as foes.

A   Aadd9/11 A   Aadd9/11 A
Maybe   it's not too late

  A   Aadd9/11   A
To learn how to love

            A   Aadd9/11   A
And forget how to hate.

Chorus 1

F#5   E6 F#5   D5
Men - tal wounds not healing

F#5   E6 F#5   D5
Life's a bitter shame

  A5   E5   F#5 E6 F#5
I'm going off the rails on a crazy train

  A5   E5   F#5 E6 F#5
I'm going off the rails on a crazy train.

Link 1

| A5 E5 | F#5 E6 F#5 | D5 E5 ‖

| A | Aadd9/11 A | A | Aadd9/11 A ‖

Verse 2

```
        A                      Aadd9/11  A
I've listened to preachers
        A             Aadd9/11  A
I've listened to fools
        A                      Aadd9/11     A
I've watched all the dropouts
                 A         Aadd9/11     A
Who make their own rules
        A              Aadd9/11  A
One person con - ditioned
               A          Aadd9/11  A
To rule and con - trol
        A           Aadd9/11  A
The media sells  it
                 A         Aadd9/11  A
And you live the role.
```

Chorus 2

```
F#5    E6 F#5        D5
Men - tal wounds still screaming
F#5    E6 F#5      D5
Driv - ing me in - sane
       A5          E5            F#5
I'm going off the rails on a crazy train
       A5          E5            F#5   E6 F#5
I'm going off the rails on a crazy train.

| A5  E5 | F#5  E6  F#5 | D5  E5 ‖
```

Bridge

```
F#5              A5        E5   F#5    N.C.   D5  E5
   I know that things are going wrong for me
F#5         A5    E5          F#5
  You gotta listen to my words
D5    E5
Yeah___.
```

Guitar solo

```
‖: F#5   E5 | D5   C#5| B5 A5 G#5| F#5   :‖ Play 3 times
   (Yeah.)
|  F#5   E5 | D5   C#5| B5 A5 G#5| E5   ‖
```

Link 2

```
| F#5    | A5 E5 | F#5   | D5 E5 |
| F#5    | A5 E5 | F#5   | D5 E5 ‖
(Guitar riff)
| A        | Aadd9/11 A | A        | Aadd9/11 A  ‖
```

Verse 3

    A   **Aadd9/11** **A**
Heirs of a cold war

                 A   **Aadd9/11**   **A**
That's what we've be - come

    A   **Aadd9/11** **A**
In - heriting troubles

              A   **Aadd9/11** **A**
I'm mentally numb_____

A   **Aadd9/11**   **A**   **A**   **Aadd9/11** **A**
Crazy,   I just cannot bear

    A   **Aadd9/11 A**
I'm living with something

    A   **A**   **Aadd9/11 A**
 That just isn't fair.

Chorus 3

F♯5   **E6 F♯5**   **D5**
Men - tal wounds not healing

F♯5   **E6 F♯5**   **D5**
Who and what's to blame?

    A5   **E5**   **F♯5**
I'm going off the rails on a crazy train

    A5   **E5**   **F♯5** **E6 F♯5**
I'm going off the rails on a crazy train.

| **A5** **E5** | **F♯5** **E6** **F♯5** | **D5** **E5** ‖

Outro

‖: **F♯5** | **A5** **E5** | **F♯5** | **D5 E5** :‖
                                  to fade

A Dangerous Meeting

Words & Music by
King Diamond & Hank Sherman

Intro

‖: E5 | E5 | G5 | E5 | [1.] E5 | D :‖ [2.] E5 ‖

‖: E5 | E5 | E5 | E5 :‖

riff 1

G F♯	G A B C B A
3fr 2fr	3fr open 2fr 3fr 2fr open
⑥ ⑥	⑥ ⑤ ⑤ ⑤ ⑤ ⑤

| E5 | G5 E5 | E5 |

‖: E5 | G5 E5 | E5 | riff 1 :‖

Verse 1

E5   G5   E5   riff 1
    Tonight the circle is meeting again
         E5   G5   E5   riff 1
Who will be the first to fall in trance?
E5   G5   E5   riff 1
   In here no - body is sensing the rain
      E5   G5   E5   riff 1
To - night the spirit will glance.

Link 1

‖: E5   E5   D5   D5 C♯5 | G5   F♯5   A5 G5 :‖

Play 4 times

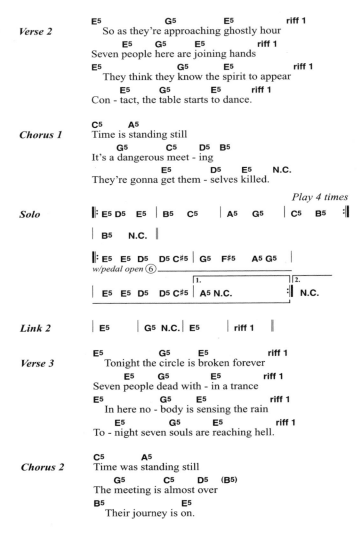

Verse 2

E5   G5   E5   riff 1
So as they're approaching ghostly hour

     E5   G5   E5   riff 1
Seven people here are joining hands

E5   G5   E5   riff 1
They think they know the spirit to appear

      E5   G5   E5   riff 1
Con - tact, the table starts to dance.

Chorus 1

C5   A5
Time is standing still

    G5   C5   D5 B5
It's a dangerous meet - ing

         E5   D5   E5   N.C.
They're gonna get them - selves killed.

Play 4 times

Solo

‖: E5 D5 E5 | B5 C5 | A5 G5 | C5 B5 :‖

| B5   N.C. ‖

‖: E5 E5 D5 D5 C#5 | G5 F#5 A5 G5 |
w/pedal open ⑥

                         ⌐1.   ⌐2.
| E5 E5 D5 D5 C#5 | A5 N.C. :‖ N.C.

Link 2

| E5 | G5 N.C.| E5 | riff 1 ‖

Verse 3

E5   G5   E5   riff 1
Tonight the circle is broken forever

    E5   G5   E5   riff 1
Seven people dead with - in a trance

E5   G5   E5   riff 1
In here no - body is sensing the rain

     E5   G5   E5   riff 1
To - night seven souls are reaching hell.

Chorus 2

C5   A5
Time was standing still

    G5   C5   D5 (B5)
The meeting is almost over

B5   E5
Their journey is on.

Interlude
   | (E5) | E5   A5 | E5 | E5 A5 C5 ‖

riff 2

‖: E5   Em   E5   D | E5   Em   N.C. (E5) :‖

Play 4 times

Bridge

w/riff 2   w/riff 2
  Oh,——— they should have known

w/riff 2   w/riff 2
  Not to play with the powers of Hell.

‖: E5   F♯5 | G5   A5 | B5   E5 | E5 F♯5 G5 C5 |

| E5   F♯5 | G5   A5 | B5   E5 | E5 F♯5 C5 B5 :‖

| E5 | G5   E5 | E5 | riff 1   ‖

Outro

      E5   G5   E5   riff 1
Some people   have lost their way

      E5   G5 E5   riff 1
Some people have lost their mind.

| E5 | G5 E5 | E5 | riff 1 | N.C. E5 ‖
w/ad lib. vocal ⌐——————————⌐

Detroit Rock City

Words & Music by
Paul Stanley & Bob Ezrin

Tune down a semitone

Guitar & bass riff

Intro
| (C#5) | (C#5) | (C#5) | (C#5) (E5) |

| A | A E5 | B | B | (riff) C#5 | (riff) C#5 |

| (riff) C#5 | (riff) C#5 E5 | A | A E5 | B | B |

Verse 1

C#5
I feel uptight on a Saturday night

E5   B5   F#5
Nine o'clock, the radio's the only light

C#5
I hear my song and it pulls me through

E5   B5
Comes on strong, tells me what I got to do,

F#5
I got to:

Chorus 1

E5   A
Get up,

Everybody's gonna move their feet

E5   B
Get down,

Everybody's gonna leave their seat

C#5(riff)
    You gotta lose your mind in Detroit Rock City.

cont.

E5 A
Get up,

Everybody's gonna move their feet
E5 B
Get down,

Everybody's gonna leave their seat.

Verse 2

C#5
Getting late, I just can't wait
E5   B5   F#5
Ten o'clock and I know I gotta hit the road
C#5
First I drink, then I smoke
E5   B5   F#5
Start the car, and I try to make the midnight show.

Chorus 2

E5 A
Get up,

Everybody's gonna move their feet
E5 B
Get down,

Everybody's gonna leave their seat.

Instrumental

(riff)						
C#5	C#5	C#5	C#5	C#5	C#5	C#5
D#5	D#5	C#5	C#5	F#5	E5	E5 A
A	A	E5 B	B	B		

Verse 3

C#5
Movin' fast, doin' 95
E5   B5   F#5
Hit top speed but I'm still movin' much too slow
C#5
I feel so good, I'm so alive
E5   B5
I hear my song playin' on the radio
F#5
It goes:

Chorus 3   E⁵ A
          Get up,

          Everybody's gonna move their feet
          E⁵ B
          Get down,
                                        G♯5   C♯5
          Everybody's gonna leave their seat.

                Drum solo
Instrumental | N.C. | N.C. | N.C. | N.C. |

                Guitar solo   *x3*
                ‖: N.C. | N.C. | N.C. | N.C. :‖

                | N.C. | N.C. | N.C. | N.C. | N.C. (E5) |

                | A | A (E5) | B | B |

                C♯5(riff)   E⁵
                You gotta lose your mind in Detroit Rock City.

                | A   E5 | B | B |

                C♯5
Verse 4   Twelve o'clock, I gotta rock
                        E⁵   B⁵   F♯5
                There's a truck ahead, lights starin' at my eyes.
                C♯5
                Oh my God, no time to turn
                 E⁵   B⁵
                I got to laugh 'cause I know I'm gonna die.
                F♯5
                Why.

                E⁵ A
Outro chorus Get up,

                Everybody's gonna move their feet
                E⁵ B   G♯5 C♯5
                Get down.

                Drum solo
                | N.C. | N.C. | N.C. |

                E⁵ A
                Get up,

                Everybody's gonna move their feet
                E⁵ B   G♯5 C♯5
                Get down.

Dirty Deeds Done Dirt Cheap

Words & Music by
Angus Young, Malcolm Young & Brian Johnson

Intro ‖: E   G5 │ G5 E A5 │ A5 E D5 │ D5 E   :‖

Play 3 times

│ E   G5 │ G5 E A5 │ A5 E D5 │ D5 E D5 ‖

Verse 1

　　　　　　E
If you're havin' trouble with your high school head,
　　　　　　　　　　　　　　　　D5
He's givin' you the blues,
E
　　You wanna graduate but not in 'is bed,
　　　　　　　　　　　　　D5
Here's what you gotta do:
E
　　Pick up the phone, I'm always home,

Call me any time.
D5　　　　E　　　　　D5　　　　　　E　　　　　D5
Just ring thirty-six, twenty-four, thirty-six, hey,
E　　　　　　D5　 E
　　I lead a life of crime.

Chorus 1

A　　　　　　　　　　G5　A
Dirty Deeds Done Dirt Cheap,
E　　　　　　　　　D5　E
Dirty Deeds Done Dirt Cheap,
A　　　　　　　　　　G5　A
Dirty Deeds Done Dirt Cheap,
E
Dirty Deeds and they're Done Dirt Cheap,
　　　　　　　　　　　　　　　D5
Dirty Deeds and they're Done Dirt Cheap.

Verse 2

E
   You got problems in your life of love,

             D5
You got a broken heart.

E
   He's double dealin' with your best friend,

                 D5
That's when the teardrops start, fella.

E
   Pick up the phone, I'm here alone,

            D5
Or make a social call.

E   D5 E   D5
   Come right in,   forget about him,

E   D5   E
   We'll have ourselves a ball.

Chorus 2

A   G5 A
Dirty Deeds Done Dirt Cheap,

E   D5 E
Dirty Deeds Done Dirt Cheap,

A   G5 A
Dirty Deeds Done Dirt Cheap,

E
Dirty Deeds and they're Done Dirt Cheap,

                          D5
Dirty Deeds and they're Done Dirt Cheap.

Solo

| B | B A | B | B A | B | B A |

| B | B D5 | E   G5| G5 E A5| A5 E D5| D5 E |

| E   G5| G5 E A5| A5 E D5| D5 E D5 ‖

Verse 3

       E
If you   got a lady and you want her gone,

             D5
But you ain't got the guts.

E
   She keeps naggin' at you night and day,

             D5
Enough to drive you nuts.

E
   Pick up the phone, leave her alone,

             D5
It's time you made a stand.

       E   D5   E   D5
    For a fee   I'm happy to be

       E   D5   E
    Your back door man.

Chorus 3

    A   G5 A
    Dirty Deeds Done Dirt Cheap,

    E   D5 E
    Dirty Deeds Done Dirt Cheap,

    A   G5 A
    Dirty Deeds Done Dirt Cheap,

    E
    Dirty Deeds and they're Done Dirt Cheap,

    Dirty Deeds and they're Done Dirt Cheap.

    Dirty Deeds and they're Done Dirt Cheap,

    Dirty Deeds and they're Done Dirt Cheap.

Outro

    E   G5 E   A5 E
    Concrete shoes,   cyanide, TNT,

         D5 E
    Done Dirt Cheap.

         G5 E   A5 E
    Neckties, contracts,   high voltage,

         D5 E
    Done Dirt Cheap.

                    G5│ G5 E   A5│ A5   │
‖: Dirty Deeds

    E   D5 E
    Done Dirt Cheap. :‖ *Play 4 times*

Enter Sandman

Words & Music by
James Hetfield, Lars Ulrich & Kirk Hammett

riff C

Intro   ‖: E E G B♭ A E | E E G B♭ A E :‖   *Play 6 times*

| E5 | E5 | E5 | E5 |

riff D

‖: E5 E B♭ A F5 | E5 E B♭ A F5 |

| E5 E B♭ A F5 | E5 E B♭ A F5 :‖

Play 3 times

riff A

‖: E5 E B♭ A | E5 E B♭ A |

| E5 E B♭ A | G5 E5 F♯5 E5 F♯5 G5 F♯5 :‖

Verse 1

E5   F5   E5
    Say your prayers, little one,

        F5   E5
Don't forget, my son,

            G5   E5 F♯5 E5 F♯5 G5 F♯5
To include every - one.

E5   F5   E5
Tuck you in, warm with - in,

         F5   E5
Keep you free from sin,

            G5   E5 F♯5 E5 F♯5 G F♯5
Till the sandman he comes.

riff B

F♯5 F♯ C B   F♯5 F♯ C B   F♯5 F♯ C
Pre-chorus 1   Sleep with one eye open,

B   F♯5 F♯ C B
Gripping your pillow   tight.

Chorus 1	**F#5 C B5 F#5 C B5** Ex - it: light,
	F#5 C B5 E5 En - ter: night.
	F#5 C B5 E5 Take my hand,
	** F#5 E5 F#5 G5 F#5 E5** We're off to Nev - er - never Land.

Link 1   ‖: riff A :‖

Verse 2	**E5 F5 E5** Something's wrong, shut the light,
	** F5 E5** Heavy thoughts to - night,
	** G5 E5 F#5 E5 F#5 G5 F#5 E5** And they aren't of Snow White.
	** F5 E5** Dreams of war, dreams of liars,
	** F5 E5** Dreams of dragon's fire,
	** G5 E5 F#5 E5 F#5 G5 F#5** And of things that will bite.

Pre-chorus 2   As Pre-chorus1

Chorus 2   As Chorus 1

Solo   ‖: riff A :‖

      ‖: riff B | riff B   :‖

      | F#m C B5 | F#m C B5 | F#m C B5 | E5 | F#5 C B5 | E5

      | gtr. fill   ‖

Link 2 | E5 | E5 | E5 | E5   ‖

Bridge

Riff C
Now I lay me down to sleep,

Pray the Lord my soul to keep.

If I die be - fore I wake,

Pray the Lord my soul to take.
Riff B
Hush little baby, don't say a word,

And never mind that noise you heard,

It's just the beasts un - der your bed,

In your closet, in your head.

Chorus 3

| F#5 | C | B5 F#5 | C | B5 |

    Ex - it: light,

| F#5 | C | B5 E5 |

    Ent - er: night,

| F#5 | C | B5 E5 |

   Grain of sand.

Chorus 4   As Chorus 1

Link 3

| E5 E B A | E5 E B A | E5 E B A |

| E5 E B A | E5 E B A |

    Yeah, yeah.

| E5 E B A | E5 E B A | G5 E5 G#5 E5 F#5 G5 F#5 |

    Yo.

| riff D | riff D ‖

riff D

Outro   We're off to Never - never Land.

   riff D
‖: Please take my hand,

We're off to Never - never Land.
riff D
Take my hand,

We're off to Never - never Land. :‖ *Repeat ad lib. to fade*

Epic

Words & Music by
Mike Patton, Roddy Bottum, Mike Bordin,
Billy Gould & Jim Martin

Intro | E | B/E | C/E   D/E | E   G5   F♯5   G5 ‖

                   (E)

Verse 1   Can you feel it, see it, hear it today?

                If you can't, then it doesn't matter anyway.

                You will never understand it 'cause it happens too fast,

                And it feels so good it's like walking on glass.

                It's so cool, it's so hip, it's alright;

                It's so groovy, it's outta sight.

                You can touch it, smell it, taste it so sweet,

                But it makes no difference 'cause it knocks you off your feet.

                E   **B/E**   **C/E**   **D/E** | **E**   **G5 F♯5 G5** ‖

Chorus 1   You want it all but you can't have it.

                (E)

Verse 2   It's crying, bleeding, lying on the floor,

                So you lay down on it and you do it some more.

                E7♯9

                You've got to share it, so you dare it

                Then you bare it and you tear it.

	E B/E C/E	E5 G5 F♯5 G5 ‖
Chorus 2	You want it all but you can't have it.	
	E B/E C/E	E5 G5 F♯5 G5 ‖
	It's in your face but you can't grab it.	

          (E)

Verse 3   It's alive, afraid, a lie, a sin,

It's magic, it's tragic, it's a loss, it's a win.

E7♯9
It's dark, it's moist, it's a bitter pain.

It's sad it happened and it's a shame.

	E B/E C/E	E5 G5 F♯5 G5 ‖
Chorus 3	You want it all but you can't have it.	
	E B/E C/E	
	It's in your face but you can't grab it.	

Bridge 1

E5   G5 F♯5 G5 E5
What is it?   It's it.

               G5 F♯5 G5 E5
What is it?   It's it.

               G5 F♯5 G5 E5
What is it?   It's it.

               G5 F♯5 G5 E5 | E |
What is it?   It's   it.

E	E	E	

C/E	C/E	D/E	D/E ‖

Instrumental	Em	Em	C/E	C/E
	D/E	D/E	Em	Em ‖

Bridge 2

E5   G5 F♯5 G5 E5
What is it?   It's it.

               G5 F♯5 G5 E5
What is it?   It's it.

               G5 F♯5 G5 E5
What is it?   It's it.

               G5 F♯5 G5
What is it?

Chorus 4
    E   B/E   C/E
You want it all but you can't have it.
    E   B/E   C/E
It's in your face but you can't grab it.

Coda
         Em
‖: It's it.
            B/E
What is it? It's it.
            C/E
What is it? It's it.
                G5   F♯5   E5
What is it? It's it, (yeah, yeah, yeah). :‖ *Play 3 times*
      Em
It's it.
            B/E
What is it? It's it.
            C/E
What is it? It's it.
                G5   F♯5   E5
What is it? It's it, (yeah, yeah, yeah).
      Em | B/E | C/E | C/E   ‖
It's it.

Piano outro
‖: Em | Em | C | C   :‖

| Em | Em | C7 | C | Em   ‖

Fade To Black

Words & Music by
Words & Music by James Hetfield, Lars Ulrich,
Cliff Burton & Kirk Hammett

Intro

‖: Bm | Bm/A | Bm | A/C♯ :‖

Play 5 times

| F6 E | E | |

‖: Am | C | G | Em :‖

Play 4 times

Verse 1

Am   C
Life it seems will fade away,

G   Em
Drifting further ev'ry day.

Am   C
Getting lost within myself,

G   Em
Nothing matters, no-one else.

Am   C
I have lost the will to live,

G   Em
Simply nothing more to give.

Am   C
There is nothing more for me.

G   Eaug
Need the end to set me free.

Interlude 1

‖: A5 | C5 | A5   D5 | E5 | |

| A5 | C5 | A5   G5 F♯5 | E5 :‖

Interlude 2

‖: Am | C | G | Em :‖

Verse 2

Am   C
Things not what they used to be,

G   Em
Missing one inside of me.

Am   C
Deathly lost, this can't be real,

G   Em
Cannot stand this hell I feel.

Am   C
Emptiness is filling me

G   Em
To the point of agony.

Am   C
Growing darkness taking dawn,

G   Eaug
I was me but now he's gone.

Interlude 3   As Interlude 1

Interlude 4   ‖: D5 E5 | D5 E5 G5 F♯5 | D5 | D5 :‖

Bridge 1

D5 E5   D5 E5   G5 F♯5   D5
No one but me can save myself but it's too late.

D5   E5   D5 E5   G5   F♯5 D5
Now I can't think, think why I should even try.

Interlude 5   As Interlude 4

Bridge 2

D5 E5   D5 E5   G5 F♯5   D5
Yesterday seems as though it nev-er existed.

D5   E5   D5 E5 G5 F♯5   D5
Death greets me warm, now I will just say goodbye.

Interlude 6   ‖: E5 | E5 G5 F♯5 | E5   D5 | D5 :‖

Outro solo   ‖: B5 | B5 | A5 | A5 |

                            | G5 | G5 | A5 | A5 :‖

Repeat to fade

Fear Of The Dark

Words & Music by
Steve Harris

Intro

| Dm | C5 | Dm | C5 |

| A5 | G5 | A5 | F5 G5 ||

||: D5 B♭5 | C5 B♭5 C5 | D5 B♭5 | C5 :||

Verse 1

D5   B♭5   C5
I am the man who walks alone,
                B♭5   C5   D5
And when I'm walking a dark road,
                    B♭5   C5   B♭5 C5
At night or strolling through the park.
D5   B♭5   C5
When the light begins to change,
                  F5   G5   D5
I sometimes feel a little strange,
             B♭5   C5
A little anxious when it's dark.

Chorus 1

                B♭5 C5   D5
Fear of the dark. Fear of the dark.
C5   B♭5   F5   G5   D5
I have a constant fear that someone's always near.
               B♭5 C5   D5   C5
Fear of the dark. Fear of the dark.
             B♭5   F5   G5   D5
I have a phobia that someone's always there.

Link 1

||: D5 | B♭5| B♭5 | C5|
(faster)
| D5 | D5 | D5 | D5 :||

Verse 2

D5   B♭5
Have you run your fingers down the wall,
            C5
And have you felt your neck skin crawl
         D5
When you're searching for the light?
              B♭5
Sometimes when you're scared to take a look
       C5
At the corner of the room,
             D5
You've sensed that something's watching you.

Chorus 2

    B♭5 C5   D5
Fear of the dark. Fear of the dark.
C5   B♭5   F5   G5   D5
I have a constant fear that something's always near.
      B♭5 C5   D5   C5
Fear of the dark. Fear of the dark.
    B♭5   F5   G5   D5
I have a phobia that someone's always there.

Verse 3

D5   B♭5   C5
Have you ever been alone at night,
        D5   C5   D5
Thought you heard footsteps behind
      B♭5   C5
And turned around and no ones there?
D5   B♭5   C5
And as you quicken up your pace,
      F5   G5   D5
You find it hard to look again
     B♭5   C5
Because you're sure there's someone there.

Chorus 3   As Chorus 2

Interlude

‖: D5 | B♭5 B♭5 | C5 |

| D5 | D5 | D5 | D5 :‖

                                      x4

‖: D5 | B♭5 | G5 B♭5 C5 | D5 :‖

Solo

| D5 | D5 | B♭5 C5 | D5 |

| D5 | D5 | B♭5 C5 | D5 |

| F♯5 | F♯5 | D5 E5 | F♯5 |

| F♯5 | F♯5 | D5 E5 | F♯5 |

| D5 | D5 | B♭5 | B♭5 |

| G5 | A5 | Dsus2 | Dsus2 ‖

Bridge

   D5   B♭5

‖: Fear of the Dark. Fear of the dark.

   G5   A5   Dsus2

Fear of the dark. Fear of the dark.   :‖

Link 2

As link 1

Verse 4

D5   B♭5   C5

Watching horror films the night before,

               F5   G5   D5

Bedating witches and folklore

                    B♭5   C5

The unknown troubles on your mind.

D5   B♭5   C5

Maybe your mind is playing tricks,

             F5   G5   D5

You sense and suddenly eyes fix

      B♭5   C5

On dancing shadows from behind.

	B♭5 C5 **D5**

Chorus 4   B♭5 C5   D5
         Fear of the dark. Fear of the dark.
         C5 **B♭5**   **F5**   **G5** **D5**
         I have a constant fear that someone's always near.
              B♭5 C5   **D5** **C5**
         Fear of the dark. Fear of the dark.
            B♭5 **F5**   **G5**   **D5**
         I have a phobia that someone's always there.

Chorus 5   As Chorus 4

Link 3 | **D5** **B♭5** |**C5** **B♭5 C5** | **D5** **B♭5**| **C5** ||

         D5   **B♭5**   **C5**
Outro   When I'm walking a dark road
            F5   **G5**   **D5**
         I am the man who walks alone.

Feel Good Hit
Of The Summer

Words & Music by
Joshua Homme & Nick Oliveri

Intro ‖: (B♭5) | (B♭5) | (B♭5) | (B♭5) :‖

Chorus 1

B♭5
Nicotine, Valium, Vicodin, Marijuana,

Ecstasy and Alcohol, ___

Nicotine, Valium, Vicodin, Marijuana,

Ecstasy and Alcohol, ___

Nicotine, Valium, Vicodin, Marijuana,

Ecstasy and Alcohol, ___

Nicotine, Valium, Vicodin, Marijuana,

                             D♭5
Ecstasy and Alcohol. _____

B♭5   D♭5
C-C-C-C-C-Co-caine.

Verse 1 | B♭5 | B♭5 | B♭5 | E♭5 |
                                      C-C-C-C-C-Co-caine.

              | B♭5 | B♭5 | B♭5 | E♭5 |
                                      Co - Co - caine.

              | B♭5 | B♭5 | B♭5 | E♭5 ‖
                                      C-C-C-C-C-Co-caine.

Link | (B♭5) | (B♭5) | (B♭5) | (B♭5) ‖

Guitar solo | D♭5 | D♭5 | D♭5 | D♭5 |

                 | (B♭5) | (B♭5) | (B♭5) | (B♭5) ‖

Chorus 2

B♭5
Nicotine, Valium, Vicodin, Marijuana,

Ecstasy and Alcohol, ___

Nicotine, Valium, Vicodin, Marijuana,

Ecstasy and Alcohol, ___

Nicotine, Valium, Vicodin, Marijuana,

Ecstasy and Alcohol, ___

Nicotine, Valium, Vicodin, Marijuana,

D♭5
Ecstasy and Alcohol. _____

B♭5   D♭5
C-C-C-C-C-Co-caine.

Verse 2

| B♭5 | B♭5 | B♭5 | E♭5 |
C-C-C-C-C-Co-caine.

| B♭ | B♭5 | B♭5 | D♭5 ||
Co - Co - caine.

Chorus 2

B♭5
Nicotine, Valium, Vicodin, Marijuana,

Ecstasy and Alcohol, ___

Nicotine, Valium, Vicodin, Marijuana,

Ecstasy and Alcohol, ___

Nicotine, Valium, Vicodin, Marijuana,

Ecstasy and Alcohol, ___

Nicotine, Valium, Vicodin, Marijuana,

Ecstasy and Alcohol. _____

D♭5
C-C-C-C-C-Co-caine.

The Fight Song

Words & Music by
Brian Warner & John Lowery

| **Intro** | | F#5 E5 F#5 A5 | F#5 E5 F#5 A5 | |

Riff 1

:‖ F#5 E5 F#5 A5	F#5 E5 F#5 A5	
				x3
	F#5 E5 F#5 A5	F#5 E5 F#5 E5 ‖:

Riff 1

Verse 1
    Nothing suffocates you more than

The passing of everyday human events.

Riff 1
    And isolation is the oxygen mask,

You make your children breath in to survive.

Riff 1

Chorus 1
    And I'm not a slave to a god that doesn't exist.

Riff 1
    And I'm not a slave to a world that doesn't give a shit.

B5   **A5**

Bridge 1
    And when we were good,

B5   **A5**
    You just close your eyes.

D5   **B5**
    So now we are bad,

A5   **E5**   **(F5)**
    We'll scar your mind

Riff 1
    Fight, fight, fight, fight.

Fight, fight, fight, fight.

Verse 2

Riff 1
　　You'll never grow up to be a big rock star,

Celebrated victim of your fame.

Riff 1
　　They'll just cut our wrists like cheap coupons,

And say that death is on sale today.

Bridge 2

B5　　　　　　**A5**
　　And when we were good,

B5　　　　　　　　**A5**
You just close your eyes.

D5　　　**B5**
　　So when we are bad,

A5　　　　　　　　**E5**　　　　(**F5**)
　　We'll scar your mind.

Chorus 2　　As Chorus 1

Middle

C5　　　　　　　　　　　**D5**　**A5**
　　The death of one is a tragedy,

C5　　　　　　　　**A5**
　　The death of one is a tragedy,

C5　　　　　　　　　　　**D5**　**A5**
　　The death of one is a tragedy,

C5　　　　　　　　　　　**A5**　　**B5**
　　The death of a million is just a sta - tis - tic.

Chorus 3　　As Chorus 1

Chorus 4　　As Chorus 1

Outro

Riff 1
　　Fight, fight, fight, fight.

Fight, fight, fight, fight.

Godzilla

Words & Music by
Donald Roeser

riff 1

Intro

‖: F#5   B5 C#5 G#5 | A5   D#5 E5 B5 |

| F#5   B5 C#5 G#5 | A5   D#5 E5 B5 :‖

Verse 1

F#5 w/riff 1
With a purposeful grimace and a terrible sound

                                        F#5 w/riff 1
He pulls the spitting high tension wires down

F#5 w/riff 1
Helpless people on a subway train

                                        F#5 w/riff 1
Scream bug-eyed as he looks in on them

   F#5 w/riff 1
He picks up a bus and he throws it back down

As he wades through the buildings

                               F#5 w/riff 1
Toward the center of town.

Chorus 1

E5
Oh no, they say he's got to go

           F#5
Go go God - zilla, yeah

E5
Oh no, there goes Tokyo

           F#5
Go go God - zilla, yeah.

Solo

‖: F#5   B5 C#5 G#5 | A5   D#5 E5 B5 |

| F#5   B5 C#5 G#5 | A5   D#5 E5 B5 :‖

Chorus 2   As Chorus 1

Interlude	**F#5 (N.C.)** w/ad lib. vocal
(Spoken)	*Rinji news o moshiagemasu!* *Rinji news o moshiagemasu!* *Godzilla ga ginza hoomen e mukatte imasu!* *Daishkyu hinan shite kudasai!* *Daishkyu hinan shite kudasai!*

Chorus 3	**E5**
	Oh no, they say he's got to go
	      F#5
	Go go God - zilla, yeah
	E5
	Oh no, there goes Tokyo
	      F#5
	Go go God - zilla, yeah.

Outro

| F#5   B5 C#5 G#5 | A5   D#5 E5 B5 |

| F#5   B5 C#5 G#5 | A5   D#5 E5 B5 |

F#5 w/riff 1
‖: History shows again and again

                                F#5 w/riff 1
How nature points up the folly of men

| ⌐1, 2, 3. | ⌐4.

                 N.C.
Godzilla! :‖ Godzilla!

Girls, Girls, Girls

Words & Music by
Nikki Sixx, Tommy Lee & Mick Mars

Tune guitar down a tone

Intro

$\|$: G5 | G5 | G5 | G5 :$\|$

$\|$: D4 E4 D4 C#4 G(r) F#(r) E(r) | E5 |

| D4 E4 D4 C#4 G(r) F#(r) E(r) | E5 :$\|$

Verse 1

```
A5                    A5     A4/A
Friday night and I need a fight
A5                    A5          B4/A
My motorcycle and a switchblade knife,
A5                    A5          A4/A
Handful of grease in my hair feels right
        A5          D8   C#8 D8 C#8 D8  C#8 D8  C#8
But what I need to make me       tight are those
```

Chorus 1

```
E5          E5
Girls, girls, girls
E5                  E5
   Long legs and burgundy lips
A5          A5
Girls, girls, girls
A5                  A5
Dancin' down on the Sunset Strip
E5          E5
Girls, girls, girls
E5          E5
   Red lips, fingertips.
```

Verse 2

A⁵   **A⁵**   **A⁴/A**
Trick or treat, sweet to eat

A⁵   **A⁵**   **B⁴/A**
On Halloween and New Year's Eve,

A⁵   **A⁵**   **A⁴/A**
Yankee girls ya just can't be beat

    A⁵   **D⁸ C♯⁸**
But you're the best when you're off your

D⁸ C♯⁸ D⁸ C♯⁸ D⁸ C♯⁸
   feet.

Chorus 2

E⁵   **E⁵**
Girls, girls, girls

    E⁵   **E⁵**
At the Dollhouse in Ft. Lauderdale

A⁵   **A⁵**
Girls, girls, girls

A⁵   **A⁵**
Rocking in Atlanta at Tattletails.

E⁵   **E⁵**
Girls, girls, girls

E⁵   **E⁵**
  Raising Hell at the 7th Veil.

Bridge

E⁵   **E⁵**
  Have you read the news

    E⁵   **E⁵**
In the Soho Trib - une

        C♯⁵
Ya know she did me

C♯⁵
  Well then she broke my heart.

B⁵   **A⁵**   **E⁵**
  I'm such a good, good boy

E⁵   **E⁵**
  I just need a new toy

E⁵
  I tell ya what, girl

C♯⁵   **C♯⁵**   **B⁵**
Dance for me, I'll keep you over-employed

B⁵   **B⁵**   **B⁵**
  Just tell me a story

E⁵   **E⁵**   **E⁵**
  You know the one I mean.

Instrumental   As introduction

A⁵   **A⁵**   **A⁴/A**
Verse 3   Crazy Horse, Paris, France
               A⁵   **A⁵**   **B⁴/A**
               For - got the names, re - member romance
               A⁵   **A⁵**   **A⁴/A**
               I got the photos, a men - age a trois
               A⁴   **D⁸ C♯⁸ D⁸ C♯⁸   D⁸ C♯⁸ D⁸ C♯⁸**
               Musta broke those Frenchies laws   with those

               E⁵   **E⁵**
Chorus 3   Girls, girls, girls
               E⁵   **E⁵**
               B-B-Body Shop and the Marble Arch
               A⁵   **A⁵**
               Girls, girls, girls
               A⁵   **A⁵**
               Tropicana's where I lost my heart.
               E⁵   **E⁵**   **E⁵**   **E⁵**
               Girls, girls, girls

               | **E⁵** | **E⁵** | **E⁵** | **E⁵** |
Link   Girls, girls, girls

               | **E⁵** | **E⁵** | **E⁵** | **E⁵** |
                    Girls, girls, girls

               | **A⁵** | **A⁵** | **A⁵** | **A⁵** | **A⁵** | **A⁵** ‖
               Girls, girls, girls   Girls, girls, girls

Outro   ‖: **E⁵** | **E⁵** | **E⁵** | **E⁵**   :‖ *Play 4 times*
                    (Guitar solo)

               | **E⁵** | **E⁵** | **E⁵** | **E⁵** |
                    Girls, girls, girls.

Hallowed Be Thy Name

Words & Music by
Steve Harris

Intro
| Em | Em | Em | Em ||

Verse 1

Em
I'm waiting in my cold cell when the bell begins to chime,

Reflecting on my past life, and it doesn't have much time.
            C   D   Em
'Cause at 5 o'clock they take me to the gallows pole,
  C   D   Em   C   D
The sands of time for me are running low.
Em   C   D   Em
Running low,   yeah.

Interlude 1
||: Em | C | D | Em :||

Verse 2

Em N.C   B5 C5
    When the priest comes to read me the last rites,
N.C   A5 D5
I take a look through the bars at the last sights.
N.C   Em   B5 C5
Of a world that has gone very wrong for me,
Em N.C   B5 C5
    Can it be there's some sort of error,
N.C   A5 D5
Hard to stop the surmounting terror,
N.C   Em B5 C5
Is it really the end, not some crazy dream.

Verse 3

Em
Somebody please tell that I'm dreaming,
C5
It's not so easy to stop from screaming,
   D5   Em B5 C5
But words escape me when I try to speak.
  Em
Tears they flow, but why am I crying,
  C5
After all, I'm not afraid of dying,
  D5   Em B5 C5
Don't believe that there is never an end.

Interlude 2   ‖: **Em** | **C** | **D** | **Em** :‖

             ‖: **Em** | **Em** | **C** | **C** :‖ *Play 4 times*

Verse 4

Em
As the guards march me out to the courtyard,
C
Someone calls from a cell "God be with you"
D   **Em**
If there's a God then why has he let me down.

As I walk all my life drifts before me,
       C
And though the end is near, I'm not sorry,
 D   **Em**
Catch my soul, 'cause it's willing to fly away.

Verse 5

Em
Mark my words, please believe my soul lives on,
         C   **D**
Please don't worry now that I have gone,
                    Em
I've gone beyond to see the truth.

When you know that your time is close at hand,
     C
Maybe then you'll begin to understand,
 D   **Em**
Life down there is just a strange illusion.

Solo

‖: Em | Em | C | C :‖

| Em | Em | Em | Em |

| C | C | Em | Em ‖

‖: Em7 C D | Em7 C D :‖

‖: Em | Em | D | D :‖ *Play 6 times*

‖: Em | Em | G :‖ *Play 4 times*

‖: Em | C | D | Em :‖

‖: Em | C | D | Em B5 C5 :‖

Outro

Em   C5   D5   Em
Yeah, yeah, yeah.   Hallowed be thy name.
Em   C5   D5   Em
Yeah, yeah, yeah.   Hallowed be thy name.

| D | C | D | Em ‖

Hard Rock Hallelujah

Words & Music by
Tomi Putaansuu

Tune Guitar D, A, D, G, B, E

Intro (Organ) | (E♭) | (Gm) | (F) | (E♭) |
| (E♭) | (Gm) | (F) | (D) |

G5   B♭5   C5   E♭5 F5 B♭5
Hard   Rock Halle - lu - jah!

G5   B♭5   E♭5   D♭5 C5 B♭5
Hard   Rock Halle-lu - jah!

G5   B♭5   C5   E♭5 F5 B♭5
Hard   Rock Halle - lu - jah!

G5   B♭5   E♭5   D♭5 C5 B♭5
Hard   Rock Halle-lu - jah!

Gm7 G6/9	Gm7 G6/9 C/G G6/9 Gm7
G6/9	Gm7 G6/9 E♭5 F5
Gm7 G6/9	Gm7 G6/9 C/G G6/9 Gm7
G6/9	Gm7 G6/9 C5 B♭5

G5

Verse 1   The saints are crippled

On this sinners' night,
F5   C5   E♭5 F5
Lost are the lambs with no guiding light.
    G5
The walls come down like thunder,

The rocks about to roll,
F5   C5   E♭5 F5
It's the Arockalypse, now bare your soul.

Pre chorus

(E♭)
All we need is lightning,
(G5)
With power and might
(F5)   (E♭)
Striking down the prophets of false.

As the moon is rising
(G5)
Give us the sign,
(F5)   (D5)   (C5)   (D5)
    Now let us rise up in awe.

Chorus

               G5   F5
Rock 'n' roll angels bring that
         G5   B♭5
Hard Rock Hallelu - jah
C5   A♭5   E♭5   F5
    Demons and angels all in one have arrived.
               G5   F5
Rock 'n' roll angels bring that
         G5   B♭5
Hard Rock Hallelu - jah
C5   A♭5   E♭5   F5
    In God's cre - ation super - natural high.

| Gm7 G6/9 |Gm7 G6/9 C/G G6/9 Gm7 |

| G6/9 |Gm7 G6/9 C5 B♭5

Verse 2

G5
    The true believers,

Thou shall be saved,
F5   C5   E♭5 F5
    Brothers and sisters keep strong in the faith.
G5
On the day of Rockoning,

It's who dares, wins,
F5   C5   E♭5 F5
You will see the jokers soon'll be the new kings.

Pre chorus 2   As Pre Chorus 1

Chorus 2   As Chorus 1

D5
    Ooh!

Interlude | N.C. | N.C. | N.C. | N.C. |

                 | N.C. | N.C. | N.C. | C5 B♭5 |

Bridge

G5
Wings on my back,
   B♭5
I got horns on my head,
C
   My fangs are sharp
   E♭5   F5
And my eyes are red.

G5
   Not quite an angel
    B♭5
Or the one that fell,
G5
   Now choose to join us
   D5   F5
or go straight to Hell.

G5   E♭5 F5 B♭5
   Hard   Rock Halle - lu - jah!
G5   D♭5 C5 B♭5
   Hard   Rock Halle - lu - jah!
G5   E♭5 F5 B♭5
   Hard   Rock Halle - lu - jah!
G5   D5
   Hard   Rock Yeah.

Chorus 3   As Chorus 1

              G5   F5
Rock 'n' roll angels bring that
   E♭5   F5
Hard Rock Hallelu - jah
C5 A♭5 E♭5 F5
(Ah.)

              G5   F5
Rock 'n' roll angels bring that
   E♭5   F5
Hard Rock Hallelu - jah
C5 A♭5 E♭5 F5
(Ah.)

     G5   B♭5   C5   E♭5 F5 B♭5
Outro   Hard   Rock Halle - lu - jah!
     G5   B♭5   E♭5   D♭5 C5 B♭5
   Hard   Rock Halle - lu - jah!
N.C.

Hells Bells

Words & Music by
Angus Young, Malcolm Young & Brian Johnson

Intro ‖: Am Asus⁴ Am⁷ │ Am⁷ Asus⁴ Am │

│ Am Asus⁴ Am⁷ │ Am⁷ A⁷sus⁴ C⁵ G/B Am :‖
Play 5 times

│ Am Asus⁴ Am⁷ │ Am⁷ Asus⁴ Am │ Am Asus⁴ G │

│ G⁵ D⁵ C⁵ G/B A⁵ ‖: A⁵ D⁵ │ D⁵ C⁵ G/B :‖

Verse 1

A⁵　　　　　　　　　　D⁵　　　　　　　C⁵ G/B
　　I'm a rollin' thunder,　pourin' rain,
A⁵　　　　　　　　　　　D⁵　　　　　　C⁵ G/B
　　I'm comin' on like a hurricane.
A⁵　　　　　　　　　　D⁵　　　　　　　　C⁵ G/B
　　My lightnin's flashin' across the sky,
A⁵　　　　　　　　　　D⁵　　　　　　　C⁵ G/B
　　You're only young but you're gonna die.

Pre-chorus 1

D⁵　　　　　　　　　　　　　　　　　C⁵　　　　G⁵
I ＿ won't take no prisoners, won't spare no lives,
D⁵　　　　　　　　　　　　　C⁵
　　Nobody's puttin' up a fight.
G⁵　E　　　　　　　　　　　　　　　　D⁵　　A⁵
　　I ＿ got my bell, I'm gonna take you to hell.
E
　　I'm gonna get you,
　　　　　　　G⁵
Satan get ya.

	Am Asus⁴ Am⁷

Chorus 1

        Am   Asus⁴ Am⁷
Hell's bells,

Asus⁴ Am   Asus⁴ Am⁷
   Yeah, hell's bells.

        A⁷sus⁴ C⁵ G/B Am   Asus⁴
You got me ringin' hell's bells.

Am⁷   Asus⁴
My temp'rature's high,

Am   Asus⁴ G⁵ | G⁵ D⁵ C⁵ G/B A⁵ ‖
Hell's bells.

Link 1 | **A⁵**   **D⁵** | **D⁵ C⁵ G/B** | **A⁵**   **D⁵ ‖**

Verse 2

D⁵ C⁵   G/B   A⁵
     I'll give you black sensations

  D⁵   **C⁵ G/B**
Up and down your spine,

A⁵   **D⁵**   **C⁵**
   If you're into evil, you're a friend of mine.

G/B A⁵   **D⁵**
See my white light flashin' as I split the night,

C⁵   **G/B A⁵**
   'Cause if   good's on the left,

      D⁵   **C⁵ G/B**
Then I'm stickin' to the right.

Pre-chorus 2

    D⁵   **C⁵**   **G⁵**
I __ won't take no prisoners, won't spare no lives,

D⁵   **C⁵**
   Nobody's puttin' up a fight.

G⁵ E   **D⁵**   **A⁵**
   I __ got my bell, I'm gonna take you to hell.

E
   I'm gonna get you,

          G⁵
Satan get ya.

Chorus 2   As Chorus 1

Guitar solo | **A⁵** | **A⁵** | **A⁵** | **A⁵** |

               | **A⁵ G⁵ A⁵ C⁵** | **C⁵ D⁵** |

                                  Play 3 times
            ‖:   **A⁵ G⁵ A⁵ C⁵** | **C⁵ D⁵** **:‖**

           | **D⁵** | **D⁵ C⁵ G⁵** | **D⁵** | **D⁵ C⁵ G⁵** |

          | **E** | **E D⁵ A⁵** | **E** | **E   G⁵**   ‖

Chorus 3

(G5)   **Am**   **Asus⁴**   **Am⁷**   **Asus⁴**
Hell's bells,   Satan's comin' to you.

Am   **Asus⁴** **Am⁷**   **A⁷sus⁴** **C5**
Hell's bells,   He's ringin' them now.

G/B **Am**   **Asus⁴** **Am⁷**   **Asus⁴**
Hell's __ bells,   the temp'rature's high,

Am   **Asus⁴** **C5**   **D5** **C5**
Hell's bells,   across the sky.

G/B **Am**   **Asus⁴** **Am⁷**   **Asus⁴**
Hell's __ bells,   they're takin' you down,

Am   **Asus⁴** **C5**   **D5** **C5** **G/B**
Hell's bells,   they're draggin' you down.

Am   **Asus⁴**   **Am⁷** **Asus⁴**
Hell's bells,   gonna split the night,

  Am   **Asus⁴**   **C5**   **D5**
Hell's bells,   there's no way to fight, yeah.

Outro

| **A5** **G5** **A5** **C5** | **C5** **D5** |

| **A5** **G5** **A5** **C5** | **C5** **D5** |
Ah,   ah, ah.

| **A5** **G5** **A5** **C5** | **C5** **D5** |

| **A5** **G5** **A5** **C5** | **D5** |
Ah.

| (**D5**) | **A5** **G5** **A5** ‖
Hell's bells.

Highway To Hell

Words & Music by
Angus Young, Malcolm Young & Brian Johnson

Intro   A ‖: N.C.   D/F♯ G5 │ N.C.   D/F♯ G5 │

│ D/F♯ G5   D/F♯ A │ A N.C.   A :‖

Verse 1

A   D/F♯ G5   D/F♯   G5
  Livin' easy,   livin' free,

D/F♯ G5   D/F♯ A
   Season ticket on a one way ride.

            D/F♯ G5   D/F♯ G5
Askin' nothin',   leave me be,

D/F♯ G5   D/F♯ A
   Takin' ev'ry - thin' in my stride.

                D/F♯ G5   D/F♯ G5
Don't need reason,   don't need rhyme,

D/F♯ G5   D/F♯ A
   Ain't nothin'   I'd rather do.

           D/F♯ G5   D/F♯ G5
Goin' down,   party time,

D/F♯ G5   D/F♯   E5
   My friends are gonna be there too.

Chorus 1

E5   A   D/A
  I'm on the highway to Hell,

G5 D/F♯   A   D/A
   On the highway to Hell.

G5   D/F♯ A   D/A
  I'm on the highway to Hell,

G5   D/F♯ A   D/A   │ D/A   A ‖
  I'm on the highway to Hell.

Verse 2

A   D/F♯ G5   D/F♯ G5
  No stop signs,   speed limit,

D/F♯ G5 D/F♯   A
   Nobody's gonna slow me down.

           D/F♯ **G5**   **D/F♯** **G5**
Like a wheel,   gonna spin it,
D/F♯ **G5**   **D/F♯** **A**
     Nobody's gonna mess me around.
          D/F♯ **G5**   **D/F♯** **G5**
Hey Satan,   pay'n' my dues,
D/F♯ **G5**   **D/F♯** **A**
     Playin' in a rockin' band.
          D/F♯ **G5**   **D/F♯** **G5**
Hey, Momma,   look at me,
D/F♯ **G5**   **D/F♯**   **E5**
I'm on my way to the promised land.

E5   **A**   **D/A**
Chorus 2   I'm on the highway to Hell,
G5   **D/F♯** **A**   **D/A**
         Highway to Hell.
G5   **D/F♯** **A**   **D/A**
I'm on the highway to Hell,
G5   **D/F♯** **A**   **D/A**
         Highway to Hell.

| **D/A**   **Dsus4/A** **D/A** |

D/A | **D/A** **Dsus4/A** **D/A** |
Don't stop me!
| **D/A**   **Dsus4/A** **D/A** ‖

Guitar solo ‖: **A**   **D/A** | **D/A**   **G5** **D/F♯** :‖ *Play 4 times*

      (G5   **D/F♯)** **A**   **D/A**
Chorus 3   I'm on the highway to Hell,
G5 **D/F♯** **A**   **D/A**
    On the highway to Hell.
G5   **D/F♯** **A**   **D/A**
I'm on the highway to Hell,
G5   **D/F♯** **A** | **N.C.** **G5** **D/F♯** ‖
I'm on the highway to...

                A   **D/A**
Chorus 4 I'm on the highway to Hell,
G5 **D/F♯** **A**   **D/A**
    On the highway to Hell.
G5   **D/F♯** **A**   **D/A**
I'm on the highway to Hell,
G5   **D/F♯** **A**   **D/A**
I'm on the highway to Hell.

                      A
And I'm goin' down all the way,

On the highway to Hell.

Here I Go Again

Words & Music by
David Coverdale & Bernie Marsden

Intro | G   D | C | G   D | C |

Verse 1

G   D   C
I don't know where I'm going

G   D   C
But, I sure know where I've been

G   D/F#
Hanging on the promises

   C/E   C   G/B
In songs of yesterday

Am   D
   An' I've made up my mind

Am   D
I ain't wasting no more time

          Em   Am
But, here I go again

C   G   Em   Am   C   D
   Here I go again.

Verse 2

G   D   C
  Tho' I keep searching for an answer

G   D   C
  I never seem to find what I'm looking for

G   D/F♯
  Oh Lord, I pray

            C/E   C   G/B
You give me strength to carry on

Am   D
  'Cause I know what it means

  Am   D   C   D
To walk along the lonely street of dreams.

Chorus 1

     G5   C5   D5   C5   D5
An' here I go again on my own

        G5   C5   D5   C5   D5
Goin' down the only road I've ever known

        G5   C5   D5   C5   G/B
Like a drifter I was born to walk alone

Am   D
  An' I've made up my mind

Am   D   C   D
  I ain't wasting no more time.

Verse 3

G   D/G   C/G   D/G
  I'm just another heart in need of rescue

G   D/G   C/G   D/G
  Waiting on love's sweet charity

G   D/F♯
  An' I'm gonna hold on

      C/E   C5 G/B
For the rest of my days

Am   D
  'Cause I know what it means

Am   D   C   D
  To walk along the lonely street of dreams

Chorus 3

     G5   C5   D5   C5   D5
An' here I go again on my own

        G5   C5   D5   C5   D5
Goin' down the only road I've ever known

        G5   C5   D5   C5   G/B
Like a drifter I was born to walk alone

cont.

     Am   **D**
     An' I've made up my mind

     Am   **D**
     I ain't wasting no more time

       C   **D** **Em**
     But here I go again.

     Am   **Em**
     Here I go again,

     Am   **Em**
     Here I go again,

     Am   **Em**   **Am**   **C**   **D**
     Here I go. ___

Instrumental | **G**   **D/G** | **C/G** **D/G** | **G**   **D/G** | **C/G** **D/G** |

                | **G**   **D/F♯** | **C/E** **C G/B** |

Link

     Am   **D**
     'Cause I know what it means

       Am   **D**   **C**   **D**
     To walk along the lonely street of dreams.

Chorus 3

       G5   **C5**   **D5** **C5** **D5**
     An' here I go again on my own

        G5   **C5**   **D5** **C5** **D5**
     Goin' down the only road I've ever known

         G5   **C5**   **D5** **C5** **G/B**
     Like a drifter I was born to walk alone.

     Am   **D**
     An' I've made up my mind,

     Am   **D**   **C**   **D**
     I ain't wasting no more time.

       G5   **C5**   **D5** **C5** **D5**
     An' here I go again on my own

        G5   **C5**   **D5** **C5** **D5**
     Goin' down the only road I've ever known

         G5   **C5**   **D5** **C5** **G/B**
     Like a drifter I was born to walk alone

     Am   **D**
     'Cause I know what it means

     Am   **D**
     To walk along the lonely street of dreams.

chorus to fade

Iron Man

Words & Music by
Terence Butler, Frank Iommi, John Osbourne & William Ward

Drums

Intro | 2 |

N.C.

(*Spoken*) I am Iron Man

Riff ‖: B5　D5　E5 | G5　D5　E5 :‖

Verse 1

B5　D5　　E5
Has he lost his mind?
G5　　　　　D5　E5
Can he see or is he blind?
B5　D5　　　E5
Can he walk at all?
G5　　　　　　D5　E5
Or if he moves　will he fall?

B5　D5　E5　　G5　D5　E5

Verse 2

B5　　D5　E5
Is he live or dead?
G5　　　　　　D5　　E5
Has he thoughts with-in his head?
B5　D5　　　E5
We'll just pass him there,
G5　　　　　　D5　E5
Why should we　ev-en care?

(B)　　　(D)　　　(E)　　　(A)　　　(B)　　　(A)

Riff ‖: B5　D5　E5 | G5　D5　E5 :‖

Verse 3

B5　D5　　　　E5
He was turned to steel
G5　　　　D5　E5
In the great magne-tic field,
B5　D5　　　E5
When he travell-ed time
G5　　　D5　E5
For the fu-ture of mankind.

Chorus   **E5**

              Nobody wants him,

      D5   **(B)**

              He just stares at the world,

      E5

              Planning his vengeance

      D5   **(B)**

              That he will still unfurl.

Riff   ‖: **B5**   **D5**   **E5** | **G5**   **D5**   **E5** :‖

      B5   **D5 E5**

Verse 4   Now the time is here

      G5   **D5**   **E5**

      For Iron Man to spread fear

      B5   **D5**   **E5**

      Vengeance from the grave

      G5   **D5**   **E5**

      Kills the people he once saved.

      E5

Chorus   Nobody wants him,

      D5   **(B)**

              They just turn their heads.

      E5

              Nobody helps him,

      D5   **N.C.(B)**

              Now he has his revenge.

Solo |**(C♯)** |**(C♯)** |

                                          x5

       ‖: **C♯5** |**C♯5** |**C♯5** |**C♯5** :‖

      |**N.C. (B)** |**N.C. (B)** |**N.C. (B)** |**N.C. (B)** |

| *Riff* | ‖: B5 D5 E5 | G5 D5 E5 :‖ |

	B5 D5 E5
Verse 5	Hea - vy boots of Lead
	G5 D5 E5
	Fills his vic - tims full of dread
	B5 D5 E5
	Run-ning as fast as they can,
	G5 D5 E5
	Iron Man lives a - gain.

	N.C.(B)	(A)	(B)	(A)	(B)	(A)
						x3
Outro	‖: N.C.	N.C.	N.C.	N.C.	:‖
						x7
	‖: E5	D5	C♯5	C5	:‖
	E5				

87

I Am The Law

Words & Music by
Frank Bello, Charlie Benante, Joe Bellardini,
Scott Rosenfeld, Daniel Spitz & Daniel Lilker

Tune Guitar D, A, D, G, B, E

Intro ‖: E5 B5 G5 | A5 G5 G5 E5 :‖ *Play 4 times*

| (E5) | (E5)   G5 F5 G5 F5 |

‖: G5 | (G5)   G5 F5 G5 F5 :‖ (G5) |

riff 1

‖: G5 F5 G5 F5 G5 F5 G5 F5 | G5 F5 G5 F5 G5 F5 A5 B♭5 :‖

Play 5 times

| G5 F5 G5 F5 ‖: G5 | (G5)   G5 F5 G5 F5 :‖

Verse 1

G5   F♯5   F5   E5
Fifteen years in the acade - my
G5   F5   E5
He was like no ca - det they'd ever seen
G5   F♯5   F5   E5
A man so hard, his veins bleed ice
G5   F5 E5
And when he speaks he never says it twice
G5   F♯5   F5   E5
They call him Judge, his last name is Dredd
G5   F5 E5
So break the law and you wind up dead
G5   F♯5   F5   E5
Truth and justice are what he's fighting for
G5   F5 E5   G5 w/riff 1
Judge Dredd the man, he is the law._____
‖: G5 F5 G5 F5 G5 F5 G5 F5 |

| G5 F5 G5 F5 G5 F5 A5   B♭5 :‖ *Play 4 times*
                    (1°) Drokk it!

| G5 F5 G5 F5 ‖

Verse 2

G5   F#5   F5   E5
With gun and bike he rules the streets

G5   F5 E5
And eve - ry perp he meets will taste defeat

G5   F#5   F5   E5
Not even death will over - come his might

G5   F5 E5
'Cause Dredd and Anderson, they won the fight

G5   F#5   F5   E5
When the Sovs started the apocalypse war

G5   F5 E5
Me - ga - city was bombed to the floor

G5   F#5   F5   E5
Dredd re - sisted, and the judges fought back

G5   F5 E5   G5 w/riff 1
Crushed the Sovs with their counter-attack._____

‖: G5 F5 G5 F5 G5 F5 G5 F5 | G5 F5 G5 F5 G5 F5 A5   B♭5 :‖
                                  ┌1.   Drokk it!

┌2.
| A5 G5 F#5 G5 ‖

Link 1

‖: E5 B5 G5 | A5 G5 G5 E5 :‖

Pre-chorus 1

E5   B5 G5   A5   G5   E5
Respect the badge – he earned it with his blood

E5   B5 G5   A5   G5   E5
Fear the gun – your sen - tence may be death because...

Chorus 1

E5
I am the law!

F5   E5
And you won't fuck around no more – I am the law

F5   E5   F5   E5
I judge the rich, I judge the poor – I am the law

E5   Em
Commit a crime I'll lock the door – I am the law

F5   E5   F5 E5   N.C.   (G5 F5 G5 F5)
Because in mega - city... I am the law.

Verse 3

G5   F#5   F5   E5
In the cursed earth where mutants dwell

G5   F5 E5
There is no law, just a living hell

G5   F#5   F5   E5
Anarchy and chaos as the blood runs red

G5   F5   E5
But this would change if it was up to Dredd

Verse 3

G5   F♯5   F5   E5
  The book of law is the Bible to him

G5   F5 E5
  And any crime committed is a sin

G5   F♯5   F5   E5
  He keeps peace with his law - giv - er

G5   F5 E5   G5 w/riff 1
  Judge, jury, and executioner.———

‖: G5 F5 G5 F5 G5 F5 G5 F5 | G5 F5 G5 F5 G5 F5 A5 B♭5 :‖
                         Drokk it!

[1.]

[2.]
| A5 G5 F♯5 G5 ‖

Link 2 ‖: E5 B5 G5 | A5 G5 G5 E5 :‖

Pre-chorus 2 As Pre-chorus 1

Chorus 2 As Chorus 1

Bridge 1 ‖: D5 C5 C♯5 | G♯root | D5 C♯5 C5 | G5 :‖

                Play 4 times

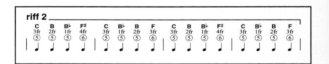

                (2°) Crime.———

riff 2

w/riff 2
(Crime) – the ultimate sin

Your iso-cube is waiting when he brings you in

Law – it's what he stands for

Crimes his only enemy and he's going to war.

Solo $\|: G5 \qquad | G5 \qquad :\|$
$\qquad\qquad\qquad\qquad$ *Play 8 times*

$\|: B \ B\flat \ A \ F \quad | \ B \ A \ B\flat \ E \quad :\|$
$\qquad\qquad\qquad\qquad$ *Play 4 times*

$\|: D5 \ C\sharp5 \ C5 \ G\sharp5 | \ D5 \ C \ C\sharp5 \ G5 :\|$
$\qquad\qquad\qquad\qquad$ *Play 4 times*

$\|: D5 \ C\sharp5 \ C5 \ G5 \ | \ D5 \ C \ C\sharp5 \ G5 :\|$
$\qquad\qquad\qquad\qquad$ *Play 4 times*

w/riff 4

Bridge 2   Crime – the ultimate sin

Your iso-cube is waiting when he brings you in

Law – it's what he stands for

Crimes his only enemy and he's going to war.

$\|: G5 \ F5 \ | \ G5 \ F5 \ | \ G5 \ F5 :\| \ A5 \ G5 \ F\sharp5 \ G5 \ \|$

$\|: E5 \ B5 \ G5 \qquad | \ A5 \ G5 \ G5 \ E5 \qquad :\|$

Pre-chorus 3   As Pre-chorus 1

Chorus 3 $\|:$ As Chorus 1 $:\|$

Outro | G5 F5 G5 F5 G5 F5 G5 F5 | G5 F5 G5 F5 G5 F5 G5 F5 |
$\qquad\qquad$ I $\qquad\qquad\qquad\qquad$ am
$\qquad$ | G5 F5 G5 F5 G5 F5 G5 F5 | A5 G5 F#5 G5 E5 N.C. ‖
$\qquad\qquad$ the $\qquad\qquad\qquad\qquad$ law.

Last Resort

Words & Music by
Tobin Esperance, Jerry Horton, Jacoby Shaddix & David Buckner

Intro

N.C.
Cut my life into pieces, this is my last resort.

E5   D5
 Suffocation, no breathing,

C5   B5 D5 | E5 D5 |
Don't give a fuck if I cut my arm bleeding.

C5   B5 D5
 This is my last resort.

| E5 D5 | C5 B5 D5 ‖

Verse 1

E5   D5   C5
 Cut my life into pieces, I've reached my last resort.

  B5   D5
Suffocation, no breathing,

E5   D5
Don't give a fuck if I cut my arm bleeding.

C5   B5 D5
 Do you even care if I die bleeding?

Verse 2

E5   D5
 Would it be wrong, would it be right,

  C5   B5   D5
If I took my life tonight? chances are that I might,

E5   D5   C5   B5 D5
 Mutilation out of sight, And I'm contemplating suicide.

Chorus 1

     E5   C5
'Cause I'm losing my sight, losing my mind,

D
Wish somebody would tell me I'm fine.

E5   C5
Losing my sight, losing my mind,

D
Wish somebody would tell me I'm fine.

Link

| E5 D5 | C5 B5 D5 ‖

Verse 3

   E5   D5
    I never realised I was spread too thin

      C5   B5   D5
   'Til it was too late and I was empty within.

          E5   D5
   Hungry,   feeding on chaos and living in sin,

   C5   B5 D5
   Downward spiral, where do I begin?

   E5   D5
    It all started when I lost my mother,

      C5   B5   D5
   No love for myself and no love for another.

          E5   D5
   Searching   to find a love upon a higher level,

        C5   B5   D5
   Finding   nothing but questions and devils.

Chorus 2   As Chorus 1

Bridge 1

   E5   C5   G5   B5
   Nothing's alright, nothing is fine.

   E5   C5   G5 B5
    I'm running and I'm cry - ing.

   E5   G5   C5   B5   E5
    I'm crying, ＿ I'm crying, ＿

      G5   C5   B5
   I'm crying, ＿ I'm crying.

   E5   D5   C5   B5   D5   E5   D5   C5   B5   D5
    I   can't go on   Liv - ing this   way.

Verse 4

   E5   D5   C5
    Cut my life into pieces,   this is my last resort.

   E5   D5
    Suffocation, no breathing,

   C5   Bm
   Don't give a fuck if I cut my arm bleeding.

Verse 5   As Verse 2

Chorus 3   As Chorus 1

Bridge 2

   E5   C5   G5   B5
   Nothing's alright, nothing is fine.

   E5   C5   G5 B5
    I'm running and I'm cry - ing.

Coda

   E5   C5   D5   E5   C5 D5
   I   can't go on liv - ing this way,

 | E5   C5   D5 | E5   C5 D5 |
                           Can't go on, ＿

 | E5   C5   D | E5   C5 |
             Living this way

 | D5 | E5 | E5   ‖
   Nothing's all   right!

Just Because

Words & Music by
Perry Farrell, Dave Navarro, Chris Chaney,
Stephen Perkins & Bob Ezrin

Intro
| B♭5 | B♭5 | B♭5 | B♭5 |

| A♭/B♭ | A♭/B♭ | A♭/B♭ | A♭/B♭ ‖

| B♭5 | B♭5 | B♭5 | B♭5 |

| A♭/B♭ | A♭/B♭ | A♭/B♭ | A♭/B♭ ‖

Verse 1

B♭5
If I were you

           A♭/B♭   **D♭/B♭**
I'd better watch out

A♭/B♭   **B♭5**
When was the last time

        A♭/B♭
You did anything

B♭   **B♭5**
Not for me

           A♭/B♭   **D♭/B♭**
Or anyone else

A♭/B♭   **B♭5**
Just be - cause

         A♭/B♭ | A♭/B♭ | A♭/B♭ | B♭ ‖
Just be - cause

Chorus 1

B♭5
You,

                          D♭/B♭
Oh, you really should have known

      B♭5
Hey you!

                  D♭/B♭
You really should have known
F5   **E♭5**
Just be - cause

      B♭5
Just be - cause

| **B♭5** | **B♭5** | **B♭5** | **B♭5** | |

| **A♭/B♭** | **A♭/B♭** | **A♭/B♭** | **B♭** | ‖

Verse 2

           B♭5
You've got the most

            A♭/B♭   **D♭/B♭** **A♭/B♭**
Ahh, but nobody loves   you
     B♭5
Nobody has to
     A♭/B♭ | **A♭/B♭** | **A♭/B♭** | **B♭** | ‖
Just be - cause

Chorus 2

B♭5
You,

                  D♭/B♭
You really should have known

     B♭5
Oh, you

                  D♭/B♭
I think you really should have known
F5   **E♭5**
Just be - cause

         B♭5
Just bec - a - a - ause

Bridge 1

| **A♭5** | **D♭** **A♭** | **B♭** | **B♭** | |
                            Oh yeah
| **A♭5** | **D♭** **A♭** | **C** | **C** | |
                      Oh, you better watch out
| **F#5** | **F#5** | **F5** | **F5** | **F#5** | |

| **F5** | **F5** | **F5** | **⁶₄ F5** | ‖

Verse 3 When we first met

A♭/B♭ **D♭/B♭**
And we passed around gifts

A♭/B♭ **B♭5**
That was a long time, ago

A♭/B♭ | **A♭/B♭** | **A♭/B♭** | **B♭** ‖
And you're feeling fit.

B♭5

Chorus 3 Yeah you,

D♭/B♭
Oh, you really should have known

B♭5
Yeah you,

D♭/B♭
Oh, you really should have known

F5 **E♭5**
Just be - cause

F5 **E♭5**
Just be - cause

B♭5
Just beca - a - a -ause

| **A♭5** | **D♭ A♭** | **B♭** | **B♭** |
Oh yeah,

Bridge 2

| **A♭5**| | **D♭ A♭**| | **C** | **A♭** | **D♭** ‖
Oh, you better watch out.

| **F♯5** | **F♯5** | **F5** | **F5** | **F♯5** |

| **F5** | **F5** | **F5** | **F5** | **F5** ‖

Mama Kin

Words & Music by
Steve Tyler

Intro ‖: **E5** | **B5** | **A5** | **E5** :‖ *Play 4 times*

| **A5** | **E5** | **A5** | **E5** |

| **E5** | **A5** | **E5** | **F♯5** |

| **B5** | **B5** | **B5** | **B5 N.C.** ‖

‖: **E5** | **B5** | **A5** | **E5** :‖

| **E5** | **E5** | **E5** |

Verse 1

E5
It ain't easy

B5
Livin' like a gypsy

A5   **E5** | **E5** |
Tell ya honey how I feel

E5
I've been dreamin'

B5
Floatin' down the stream n'

A5   **E5** | **E5** |
Losin' touch with all that's real.

Verse 2

E5
Whole earth lover

B5
Keepin' under cover

A5   **E5** | **E5** |
Never know where ya been

cont.

E5
You've been fadin'

B5
Always out paradin'

A5   **E5** | **E5** |
Keep in touch with Mama Kin.

                          A5   **E5**
Well you've always got your tail on the wag

                    A5
Shootin' fire from your mouth

                    E5
Just like a___ dragon

        A5   **E5**
You act like a perpertual drag

        F♯5
You better check it out

'Cause someday soon you'll have to

                          B5   **N.C.**
Climb back on___ a wagon

Verse 3

E5
It ain't easy

B5
Livin' like you wanna

A5   **E5** | **E5** |
It's so hard to find peace of mind, yes it is

        E5
The way I see it

        B5
You gotta say shit

A5   **E5** | **E5**   ‖
But don't forget to drop me a line.

                    A5
Said, you're bald as an egg when you're eight - een

            A5   **E5**
And workin' for your dad is just a___ drag___ yeah

        A5   **E5**
You still stuff your mouth with your dreams

        F♯5
You better check it out

'Cause someday soon you'll have to

                          B5   **B5 B5**
Climb back on the   wa - gon.

Chorus 1

E5   N.C.   B5 B5 E5
   Keep in touch with Mama Kin

N.C.   B5 B5 E5
Tell her where you've gone and been

N.C.   B5 B5 E5
Livin' out your fantasy

N.C.   B5 B5 E5
Sleepin' late and smokin' tea

A5   B5 B5 E5
Keep in touch with Mama Kin

A5   B5 B5 E5
Tell her where you've gone and been

A5   B5 B5 E5
Livin' out your fantasy

A5   G5   D5 | C5 | C5 | B5 |
Sleepin' late and smokin' tea.___

Link

| A5 | A5 | A5 | A5 ‖

Verse 4

As Verse 3

Chorus 2

E5   N.C.   B5 B5 E5
   Keep in touch with Mama Kin

N.C.   B5 B5 E5
Tell her where you've gone and been

N.C.   B5 B5 E5
Livin' out your fantasy

N.C.   B5 B5 E5
Sleepin' late and smokin' tea

A5   B5 B5 E5
Keep in touch with Mama Kin

A5   B5 B5 E5
Tell her where you've gone and been

A5   B5 B5 E5
Livin' out your fantasy

A5   G5   D5
Sleepin' late and smokin' tea.___

| C5 | D5 | Bm/E | Bm/E | (Bm/E) E5 ‖

Master Of Puppets

Words & Music by
James Hetfield, Lars Ulrich, Cliff Burton & Kirk Hammett

Intro

| E5 | D5 D♭5 C5 ‖: E E* E E♭ E |

| D5 D♭5 C5 | E B E B♭ E |

| A E A♭ E G E F♯ E :‖ *Play 4 times*

riff A _____

‖: E B E C E | C♯ E C E B |

riff B _____

| E B E C E | G5 F♯5 E G5 F♯5 E G5 F♯5 :‖

‖: riff A | riff A | riff A | riff B :‖

| E B♭ E B♭ E | B♭ E B♭ |

riff C _____

‖: E5 | E G5 A5 E B♭5 A5 G5 A5 |

| E5 | E5 G5 A5 G5 A5 :‖

Verse 1

riff C
End of passion play, crumbling away,
riff C
I'm your source of self-destruction.
riff C
Veins that pump with fear, sucking darkest clear,
riff C
Leading on your death's construction.

riff D ———————————

$F^{\sharp}5$ | $F^{\sharp}$ A5 B5 C5 B5 A5 B5 |

cont. Taste me, you will see,

$F^{\sharp}5$ | $F^{\sharp}$ A5 B5 A5 B5 ‖

More is all you need.

riff D

You're dedicated tom

             B5

How I'm killing you.

Pre-chorus 1 | E D5 E5 | E B G | C5

B5   **C5**   **E♭5**   **B5**   **E**   **D5 E5** | E B G | C5
Come crawl - ing   fast - er,

B5 C5 E♭5 B5 E   **D5 E5** | E B G | C5
O - bey your   master.

B5   **C5**   **E♭5**   **B5**   **E**   **D5 E5** | E B G | C5
Your life burns fast - er,

B5 C5 E♭5 B5
O - bey your master.

F5
Master.

    E5   **G5**   **E5**   **G5**
Chorus 1   Master of puppets, I'm pull - ing your strings,

    C5   **A**   **B5**   **A**   **A5**
Twisting your mind and smash - ing your dreams.

    D5   **G**   **C5** **G**   **B5**
Blinded by me, you can't see a thing,

    E5*   **E**   **D5 E**   **C5**
Just call my name, 'cause I'll hear you scream

    E5   **F5**
Master, Master.

    E5   **G5 E5**   **C5**
Just call my name, 'cause I'll hear you scream

    E5   **F5**
Master, Master.

Link 1 | **riff A** | **riff A** | **riff A** | **riff B** ‖

riff C
Verse 2   Needlework the way, never you betray,

riff C
Life of death becoming clearer.

cont

riff C
Pain monopoly, ritual misery,

riff C
Chop your breakfast on a mirror.

riff D
Taste me you will see,

More is all you need.

riff D
You're dedicated to

B^5
How I'm killing you.

Pre-chorus 2   As Pre-chorus 1

Chorus 2   As Chorus 1

Interlude

‖: Em D │ Cadd⁹ │ Asus² Bm⁷ B⁷ :‖

‖: Em D │ Cadd⁹ │ Asus² Bm⁷ B⁷ :‖ *Play 6 times*

‖: E⁵ D⁵ │ C⁵ │ A⁵ B⁵ B/D♯ :‖

│ E⁵ │ E⁵ │ F♯⁵ │ F♯⁵ │ F♯⁵ │ F♯⁵ ‖

Bridge

$F^{\sharp 5}$
Master, master,

Where's the dreams that I've been after?

Master, master,

You promised only lies.

Laughter, laughter,

All I hear and see is laughter.

Laughter, laughter,

G^5 $F^{\sharp 5}$
Laughing at my cries.

Fix me.

| *Solo* | 𝄆 **riff C** 𝄇 *Play 4 times* |
| | 𝄆 **riff D** 𝄇 **B5** | |

Interlude	𝄆 **E5 F5 E5 F5 E5**	**F5 E5 F5 E5 F5**	**E5 F5 E5 F5 E5**	
		F5 E5 F5 E5 B5 𝄇	
		E5 𝄁	

*chords implied by harmony*_____

| 𝄆 **E5** | **E5** | **C5** | **C5** | **E5** 𝄇 |

Play 4 times

| *Link 1* | 𝄆 **riff A** | **riff B** 𝄇 |

Verse 3

riff C
Hell is worth all that, natural habitat,
riff C
Just a rhyme without a reason.
riff C
Never-ending maze, drift on numbered days,
riff C
Now your life is out of season.
riff D
I will occupy,

I will help you die.
riff D
I will run through you,
                B5
Now I rule you, too.

Pre-chorus 3   As Pre-chorus 1

Chorus 3   As Chorus 1

| *Outro* | 𝄆 **riff C** 𝄇 *Play 4 times* |
| | **G5 F♯5 E G5 F♯5 G5 F♯5** **E5** 𝄁 |

(psycho laughter)

Mr. Crowley

Words & Music by
Ozzy Osbourne, Bob Daisley & Randy Rhoads

Intro

‖: Dm | Am | F | C | Am | Em |

| A B♭ F5 | G5 F5 E5 F5 | Asus4 | A   :‖ *x2*

Verse 1

N.C. **D5**   **(A8 F8 D5)**   **B♭5**
Mr. Crowley,   what went on in your head?

D5   **(A8 F8 D5)**   **B♭**
Oh, Mr. Crowley,   did you talk with the dead?

C
Your lifestyle to me seemed so tragic

Dm
With the thrill of it all.

C
You fooled the people with magic

B♭   **A5**
Yeah, you waited on Satan's call.

Verse 2

D5   **(A8 F8 D5)**   **B♭5**
Mr. Charming,   did you think you were pure?

D5   **(A8 F8 D5)**   **B♭**
Mr. Alarming,   in nocturnal rapport

C   **Dm**
Uncovering things that were sacred manifest on this Earth.

C
Conceived in the eye of a secret,

B♭   **A5**
And they scattered the afterbirth.

Guitar Solo	‖: Dm	B♭	C	Dm	
	B♭	Em7♭5	A5	A5	*x2* :‖

Verse 3

     Dm   **(A8 F8 Dm)**   **B♭**
Mr. Crowley,   won't you ride my white horse?
     Dm   **(A8 F8 Dm)**   **B♭**
Mr. Crowley,   it's symbolic of course.
    C
Approaching a time that is classic
        Dm
I hear that maidens call
    C
Approaching a time that is drastic
B♭   **A5**
Standing with their backs to the wall.

Instrumental	Dm	B♭	C	Dm	
	B♭	Em7♭5	A	A	

Bridge

Dm B♭   **C**
     Was it polemically sent?
Dm   **B♭**
  I wanna know what you meant
Em7♭5
  I wanna know,
A
  I wanna know what you meant, yeah.

Outro	‖: Dm	Gm	C	F	
	B♭	Em7♭5	A	A	:‖

Repeat to fade

Mother

Words & Music by
Glenn Danzig

Intro   ‖: B5 | G5 A5 | B5 | G5 A5 :‖

          B5
Verse 1   Mother
          G5   A5   B5
        Tell your children not to walk my way
          G5   A5   B5
        Tell your children not to hear my words
                   G5   A5 B5   G5 A5
      What they mean, what they say, mother.

          B5
Verse 2   Mother
          G5   A5   B5
        Can you keep them in the dark for life
          G5   A5   B5
        Can you hide them from the waiting world
          G5   A5   B5   G5 A5
        Oh_____ mother.

          B5
Verse 3   Father
          G5   A5   B5
        Gonna take your daughter out tonight
          G5   A5   B5
        Gonna show her my world
          G5   A5   B5   G5 A5
        Oh_____ father.

G5   A5   B5
Not a - bout to see your light

N.C.   B5 A5   G5
But if you wanna find hell with me

      A5   B5/F♯ N.C.
I can show you what it's like

B5   A5
Till you're bleeding

G5   A5   B5
Not a - bout to see your light

N.C.   B5   A5   G5
And if you wanna find hell with me

    A5   F♯5 N.C.
I can show you what it's...

Verse 4

B5
Mother

G5   A5   B5
  Tell your children not to hold my hand

G5   A5   B5
  Tell your children not to understand

G5   A5 B5   G5 A5
  Oh_____ mother.

Verse 5

B5
Father

G5   A5   B5
  Do you wanna bang heads with me

G5   A5   B5
  Do you wanna feel everything

G5   A5 B5   G5 A5
  Oh_____ father.

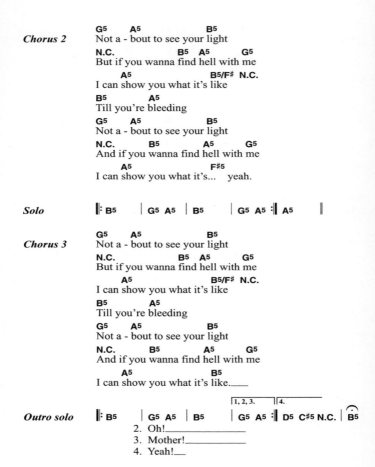

Chorus 2

G5   A5   B5
Not a - bout to see your light

N.C.   B5 A5   G5
But if you wanna find hell with me

     A5   B5/F♯ N.C.
I can show you what it's like

B5   A5
Till you're bleeding

G5   A5   B5
Not a - bout to see your light

N.C.   B5   A5   G5
And if you wanna find hell with me

     A5   F♯5
I can show you what it's... yeah.

Solo   ‖: B5 | G5 A5 | B5 | G5 A5 :‖ A5 ‖

Chorus 3

G5   A5   B5
Not a - bout to see your light

N.C.   B5 A5   G5
But if you wanna find hell with me

     A5   B5/F♯ N.C.
I can show you what it's like

B5   A5
Till you're bleeding

G5   A5   B5
Not a - bout to see your light

N.C.   B5   A5   G5
And if you wanna find hell with me

     A5   B5
I can show you what it's like.____

Outro solo   ‖: B5 | G5 A5 | B5 :‖ G5 A5 :‖ D5 C♯5 N.C. | B5
                           2. Oh!_____
                           3. Mother!_____
                           4. Yeah!__

The Nobodies

Words & Music by
Brian Warner & John Lowery

Intro

| Drums
| 2 | Am | C6 | Eaug | Am Am/G ‖

Verse 1

     Am
To - day I am dirty
   C6
I want to be pretty
      Eaug   **Am Am/G**
To - morrow, I know that I'm just dirt
     Am
To - day I am dirty
   C6
I want to be pretty
      Eaug   **Am Am/G**
To - morrow, I know I'm just dirt.___

Chorus 1

         A5
We are the nobodies
              C5
Who wanna be somebodies
         E5
When we're dead
              A5 G5
They'll know just who we are___
         A5
We are the nobodies
              C5
Who wanna be somebodies
         E5
When we're dead
             A5 G5 N.C.(Am)
They'll know just who we are.___

Verse 2

Am
Yester - day I was dirty

C6
Want - ed to be pretty

Eaug   **Am** **Am/G**
I know now that I'm forever dirt

Am
Yester - day I was dirty

C6
Want - ed to be pretty

Eaug   **Am** **Am/G**
I know now that I'm forever dirt.

Chorus 2

A5
We are the nobodies

C5
Who wanna be somebodies

E5
When we're dead

                 A5 **G5**
They'll know just who we are___

A5
We are the nobodies

C5
Who wanna be somebodies

E5
When we're dead

                 A5 **G5**
They'll know just who we are.___

Bridge

A5
Some children died the other day

F5
We fed machines and then we prayed

A5
Puked up and down in morbid faith

F5
You should have seen the ratings that day

A5
Some children died the other day

F5
We fed machines and then we prayed

A5
Puked up and down in morbid faith

F5   **E5**
You should have seen the ratings that day.___

Am		C6	

Interlude   Na na na na na.   Na na na na na.

Eaug		Am	Am/G

     Na na na na na.   Na na na na.___

                   Am

Chorus 3   We are the nobodies

                    C6

Who wanna be somebodies

                  Eaug

When we're dead

                           Am   Am/G

They'll know just who we are___

                    Am

We are the nobodies

                    C6

Who wanna be somebodies

                 E5

When we're dead

                         A5   G5

They'll know just who we are.___

                    A5

Outro   We are the nobodies

                    C5

Who wanna be somebodies

                 E5

When we're dead

                       A5   G5

They'll know just who we are___

N.C. Am	(Am)	‖

No One Knows

Words & Music by
Josh Homme, Nick Oliveri & Mark Lanegan

Tune Guitar: C F B♭ E♭ G C

Intro | Em/B | Em/B | Em | Em | Em |

| Em | Em | Em | Em | Em |

Verse 1

Em
  We get some rules to follow

That and this,
              B
These and those
E♭ | Em | Em | Em |Em
  No one knows.

Verse 2

Em
  We get these pills to swallow
                   B
How they stick in your throat
E♭ | Em | Em | Em |
  Tastes like gold.
Em   B
  Oh what you do to me
E♭   Em
  No one knows.

Chorus 1

N.C.   B5
I realise you're mine
N.C.   B5
Indeed a fool of mine
N.C.   B5
I realise you're mine
N.C.   B5
Indeed a fool am I, ah._____

Link | Em | Em | Em | Em |

Verse 3

    Em
   I journey through the desert

                B
Of the mind with no hope

E♭   **Em**
 I follow.

Verse 4

    Em
   I drift along the ocean

             B
Dead lifeboats in the sun

E♭   **Em**
 And come undone.

        B
Pleasantly caving in

E♭   **Em**
 I come undone.

Chorus 2

    N.C.   **B5**
I realise you're mine

    N.C.   **B5**
Indeed a fool of mine

    N.C.   **B5**
I realise you're mine

    N.C.   **B5**
Indeed a fool am I, ah._____

Interlude

                                          x2

‖: E5 | E5 | E5 | B5 C5 E♭5 B5 A5 B5 :‖

                  x3

‖: B5 C5 E♭5 B5 A5 B5 :‖

Bass solo | N.C. (E5) | (E5) | (E5) | (E5) |

Guitar solo | Em | Em | A5 | B5 | Em | F♯7/E

               | Em/G | Edim | Em | F♯7/E | D5 | D♯5

Bass | E (bass) | E (bass) | E (bass) | E (bass) |

Verse 5

   E (bass)
  Heaven smiles above me

Em   **B**
 What a gift here below

E♭   **Em**
 But no one knows.

           B
Gift that you give to me

E♭   **Em**
 No one knows.

Outro | Em | Em | Em ‖

Paranoid

Words & Music by
Ozzy Osbourne, Tony Iommi, Terry 'Geezer' Butler & Bill Ward

Tune guitar slightly sharp

Intro   ‖: E5 | E5 | E5 | E5   :‖

Verse 1
E5
Finished with my woman
          D5   D5   D5 E5   G
'Cos she couldn't help me with   my mind.
E5
People think I'm insane
          D5   Dsus4   D   Em
Because I am frowning all   the time.

Link 1   ‖: E5 | C5 D5 | E5 | E5   :‖

Verse 2
E5
All day long I think of things
        D5   D5   D5 E5   G
But nothing seems to sa - - tis - fy.
E5
Think I'll lose my mind
          D5   D5   D5 E5
If I don't find something to pa - - ci - fy.

Bridge
E5
  Can you help me
D5   E5   D5
  Occupy my brain? Oh yeah.

Link 2   ‖: E5 | E5 | D5 | D5 D5 E5   G   :‖

Verse 3

E5
I need someone to show me

D5   D5 D5 E5 G
The things in life that I   can't find.

E5
I can't see the things

      D5   D5 D5 E5 G
That make true happiness, I must be blind.

Guitar solo ‖: E5 | E5 | D5 | D5 D5 E5 G :‖ *Play 4 times*

Link 3 ‖: E5 | E5 | D5 | D5 D5 E5 G :‖

Verse 4

E5
Make a joke and I will sigh

   D5   D5 D5 E5 G
And you will laugh and I will cry.

E5
Happiness I cannot feel

  D5   D5 D5 E5
And love to me is so un - real.

Link 4 ‖: E5 | C5 D5 | E5 | E5 :‖

Verse 5

E5
And so as you hear these words

  D5   D5 D5 E5 G
Telling you now of my state,

E5
I tell you to enjoy life,

 D5   D5 D5 E5
I wish I could but it's too late.

Coda | E5 | E5 | D5 | D5 D5 E5 G |

    | E5 | E5 | D5 | D5 D5 E5 ‖

Party Hard

Words & Music by
Andrew W.K.

Intro   "When it's time to party we will party hard."

‖: E5 | E5 | E5 | E5 :‖

Interlude 1   ‖: E5 | E5 | E5 | B5   A5 :‖

| (E5) | (E5) ‖

| E5   B5 | A5   E/G♯ | F♯5   C♯5 | B5   D♯5   E5 |

| E5   B5 | A5   E/G♯ | F♯5   C♯5 | B5   E5   (E5) |

Verse 1
E5   B5   A5   E/G♯
You, you work all night,
     F♯5   C♯5   B5   D♯5   E5
And when you work you don't feel all right.
     E5
And when,
B5   A5   E/G♯   F♯5
When things start feeling all right
     C♯5   B5   D♯5
And everything is all right.

Bridge 1
          E5   D5   C5   E5
'Cause we will never listen to your rules, (No!)
E5*   C5   B5   E5   E5
We will never do what others do, (No!)
     C5   B5   A5   E5
We know what we want and we get it from you,
A5   B5   D♯5   E5
Do what we like and we like what we   do.

Chorus 1

E5   A5   E/G♯ A5
So let's get a party going (let's get a par - ty going),

E5   A5   D5 A5
Now it's time to party and we'll party hard (party hard).

E5   A5   E/G♯ A5
Let's get a party going (let's get a par - ty going),

E5   A5   B5 E5   D♯5 E5
When it's time to party we will always party hard.

  E5 A5 | E5 A5 | E5 A5 | B5 E5 |
Party hard.

  E5 A5 | E5 A5 | E5 A5 | F♯5 B5 E5|
Party hard.

  (E5)
Party (hard).

Interlude 2 As Interlude 1

Verse 2

E5 B5 A5   E/G♯
You, you fight that fight (that's right).

F♯5   C♯5 B5   D♯5 E5
  And when you fight you feel alright.

  E5
But when,

B5 A5   E/G♯   F♯
When things start feeling all right (all right),

  C♯5 B5   D♯5
And everything is all right.

Bridge 2 As Bridge 1

Chorus 2 As Chorus 1

Outro

  E5 A5 | E5 A5 | E5 A5 | B5 E5 |
Party hard.

  E5 A5 | E5 A5 | E5 A5 | F♯5 B5 E5|
Party hard.

  E5
Party hard.

Poison

Words & Music by
Alice Cooper, Desmond Child & John McCurry

Intro | D   ‖   *(Open duration)*

| D5 | D5 | D5 | D5 | B♭5 | D5 | B♭5 | D5 |

| B♭5 | D5 | B♭ | B♭ | D5 | D5 ‖

Verse 1

D5　　　　　B♭
　Your cruel device

F　　　　　C
　Your blood, like ice

Gm　　　　E♭
　One look could kill

B♭　　　　D
　My pain, your thrill.

Pre-chorus 1

Gm　　　　E♭　　　　　B♭
　I want to love you but I better not

F
touch, (don't touch),

Cm　　　　A♭　　　　　　E♭
　I want to hold you but my senses

B♭　　　Am
 tell me to stop,

　　　　　F　　　　　C
　I want to kiss you but I want it too

G
much, (too much),

Dm　　　　B♭
　I want to taste you but your lips

　　C
are venomous

                           Dm   B♭   F   C
Chorus 1   Poison.
                               Dm   B♭   F   C
                 You're poison running through my veins
                                   Dm   B♭ F C
                 You're poison,
                 Dm   B♭
                 I don't want to
                 F   C   B♭
                 Break these chains.

                 D5   B♭
Verse 2   Your mouth, so hot
                 F   C
                 Your web, I'm caught
                 Gm   E♭
                     Your skin, so wet
                 B♭   D
                     Black lace on sweat.

                 Gm   E♭   B♭   F
Pre-chorus 2   I hear you calling and it's needles and pins, (and pins),
                 Cm   A♭   E♭
                     I want to hurt you just to hear you
                 B♭   Am
                 Screaming my name,
                                     F
                 Don't want to touch you but
                         C   G   Dm
                 You're under my skin, (deep in)
                           B♭   F
                 I want to kiss you but your lips
                         C
                 Are venomous

	Dm B♭ F C
Chorus 2	Poison.
	Dm B♭ F C
	You're poison running through my veins,
	Dm B♭ F C
	You're poison,
	Dm B♭
	I don't want to
	F C
	Break these chains.
	B♭
	Poison.

Guitar solo | B♭5 | D5 | B♭5 | D5 | B♭5 | D5 | B♭5 | D5

	Gm E♭
Bridge 1	One look could kill
	B♭ D
	My pain, your thrill

Pre-chorus 3   As Pre-chorus 1

	Dm B♭ F C
Chorus 3	Poison.
	Dm B♭ F C
	You're poison running through my veins,
	Dm B♭ F C
	You're poison,
	Dm B♭
	I don't want to
	F C
	Break these chains.
	Gm B♭
	Poison.

Bridge 2

Dm   B♭   F   C   Dm
I want to love you but I better not touch, (don't touch),
                    B♭   F   C   Dm
I want to hold you but my senses tell me to stop,
                    B♭   F   C   Dm
I want to kiss you but I want it too much, (too much),
                    B♭   F
I want to taste you but your lips
        C
Are venomous

Outro

Dm   B♭ F C
Poison, yeah
Dm   B♭   F   C
I don't want to break these chains
Dm   B♭ F C
Poison, oh no
Dm   B♭   F   C
    Runnin' deep in - side my veins,
Dm   B♭   F   C
    Burnin' deep in - side my veins,
        Dm   B♭ F C
It's poison.
Dm   B♭   F   C
I don't want to break these chains
Dm   B♭ F C
Poison.

To fade

121

Question

Words & Music by
Serj Tankian & Daron Malakian

arpeggiated chords _____

Intro

| F♯m | F♯m | F♯m | F♯m |

| F♯m | F♯m | F♯m | F♯m |

‖: F♯5 C♯5 B5 A5 B5 G♯5 A5 | F♯5 C♯5 B5 A5 B5 G♯5 A5 :‖

Play 4 times

| F♯5 | F♯5 |

Verse 1

F♯m
   Sweet berries ready for two ghosts are no different than yo

Ghosts are now waiting for you.

B5
  Are you?

F♯m
   Sweet berries ready for two ghosts are no different than yo

Ghosts are now waiting for you.

B5
  Are you dreaming?

Bridge 1

F♯m   Dmaj7
  Dreaming the night.

F♯m   Dmaj7
  Dreaming all right.

| **Chorus 1** | F#5   B5 |

Chorus 1

F#5   B5
Do we, do we know, when we fly?
F#5   B5
When we, when we go, do we die?

| F#5 C#5 B5 A5 B5 G#5 A5 | F#5 C#5 B5 A5 B5 G#5 A5 ‖

Verse 2   As Verse 1

Bridge 2   As Bridge 1

Chorus 2   As Chorus 1

Interlude   ‖: F#5 C#5 B5 A5 B5 G#5 A5 | F#5 C#5 B5 A5 B5 G#5 A5 :‖

Play 8 times

riff A_____⌐

| F#5   C   F#5   C | F#5   C   F#5   C   ‖

Chorus 3

riff A *(x6)*   B5
Do we, do we know when we   fly?
riff A *(x6)*   B5
When we, when we go do we   die?

Outro   ‖: F#5 C#5 B5 A5 B5 G#5 A5 | F#5 C#5 B5 A5 B5 G#5 A5 :‖

| F#m | F#m | F#m   ‖

‖: F#5 C#5 B5   A5   B5   A5   G#5 A5 :‖
La   la   la   la   la   la   la   la.

Outshined

Words & Music by
Chris Cornell

Tune Guitar D, A, D, G, B, E

Play 4 times

riff 1_____

Intro ‖: D5 D5 F5 G5 F5 D5 F5 Croot │ (Croot) Ab5 G5 F5 :‖

Verse 1

D5w/riff 1
Well, I got up feeling so down

D5w/riff 1
I got off being sold out

D5w/riff 1
I've kept the movie rolling

D5w/riff 1   **D5w/riff 1**
But the story's getting old now, oh yeah.

Verse 2

D5w/riff 1
Well, I just looked in the mirror

D5w/riff 1
And things aren't looking so good

D5w/riff 1
I'm looking California

D5w/riff 1   **D5**
And feeling Minnesota, oh yeah.

Pre-chorus 1 │ D D(add11) │ D/F# Em7 │

(Em7)   **D**   **D(add11)** **D/F#**   **Em7**
So now you know who gets   mystified

D D(add11)   **D/F# Em7**   **Boct Doct D5**
(So now you know) who gets mystified.

Chorus 1

A⁵   G⁵ D⁵ F⁵   G⁵ D⁵
Show me the pow - er child

G⁵ F⁵ D⁵ F⁵
I'd like to   say

D⁵ F⁵ A♭5   G⁵ F⁵ D⁵ w/riff 2
That I'm down on my knees to - day

      A⁵   G⁵ D⁵ F⁵ G⁵ D⁵
Yeah, it gives me the but - ter - flies

G⁵   F⁵ D⁵ F⁵
Gives me a - way

D⁵ F⁵ A♭5   G⁵ F⁵ D⁵ w/riff 2
Till I'm up on my feet a - gain

              w/riff 2
Hey, I'm feeling, I'm feeling

C⁵
Outshined, outshined, outshined, outshined.

Solo

‖: D⁵ D⁵ F⁵ G⁵ F⁵ D⁵ F⁵ Croot | (Croot) A♭5 G⁵ F⁵   :‖
Play 4 times

Verse 3

D⁵w/riff 1
Someone let the dogs out

     D⁵w/riff 1
They'll show you where the truth is

    D⁵w/riff 1
The grass is always greener

D⁵w/riff 1   D⁵w/riff 1
Where the dogs are shitting, oh yeah.

Verse 4

      D⁵w/riff 1
Well, I'm feeling that I'm sober

D⁵w/riff 1
Even though I'm drinking

    D⁵w/riff 1
Well I can't get any lower

D⁵w/riff 1   D⁵
Still I feel I'm sinking, yeah.

Pre-chorus 2 As Pre-chorus 1

Chorus 2 As Chorus 1

riff 2

C D D C   C C D C   C   D
3fr 5fr 5fr 3fr   3fr 3fr 5fr 5fr 1fr open
⑤ ⑤ ⑤ ⑤ ⑤ ⑤ ⑤ ⑤ ⑤ ⑥

Breakdown 𝄆 D5* ⎪ D5* ⎪ C5 ⎪ C5 Csus4 C 𝄇

Play 3 times

𝄆 D D(add11) ⎪ D/F♯ Em7 𝄇 *Play 3 times*

⎪ Boct Doct D5 ⎪

Chorus 3

A5   G5 D5 F5   G5 D5
Show me the pow - er child

G5 F5   D5 F5
I'd like to   say

D5   F5 A♭5   G5   F5 D5 w/riff 2
That I'm down on my knees to - day

A5   G5 D5 F5   G5   D5
Yeah, it gives me the but - ter - flies

G5   F5 D5 F5
Gives me a - way

D5 F5 A♭5   G5   F5 D5 w/riff 2
Till I'm up on my feet a - gain

w/riff 2
Hey, I'm feeling, I'm feeling.

Chorus 4

C5
Show me the pow - er child

D5 F5
I'd like to   say

D5   F5 A♭5   G5   F5 D5 w/riff 2
That I'm down on my knees to - day

A5   G5 D5 F5   G5   D5
Yeah, it gives me the but - ter - flies

G5   F5 D5 F5
Gives me a - way

D5 F5 A♭5   G5   F5 D5 w/riff 2
Till I'm up on my feet a - gain

w/riff 2
Hey, I'm feeling, I'm feeling.

C5   N.C.
Outshined, outshined, outshined, outshined

Right Next Door To Hell

Words & Music by
Axl Rose, Izzy Stradlin & Timo Caltio

Tune guitar down one semitone

Intro

5

(bass guitar)

‖: E5 | E4 D4 E4 D4 E4 D4 | E5 | E4 D4 E4 :‖

Play 4 times

Verse 1

    B5   **D5**
I'll take a nicotine, caffeine, sugar fix,
    B5   **A5**   **G5** **A5**
Jesus don't ya get tired of turnin' tricks,
                 B5
But when your innocence dies
  D5
You'll find the blues,
    B5   **A5**   **G5** **A5**
Seems all our heroes were born to lose,
    B5
Just walkin' through time
  D5
You believe this heat,
    B5   **A5**   **G5** **A5**
Another empty house, another dead end street,
    B5   **D5**
Gonna rest my bones an' sit for a spell
    B5   **A5**   **G5** **A5**
This side of Heaven, this close to Hell.

Chorus 1

D5   A5
Right next door to Hell,

  E5   F#5
Why don't you write a letter to me.

    D5   A5
I said I'm right next door to Hell

  E5   F#5
An' so many eyes are on me.

D5   A5
Right next door to Hell,

  E5   F#5
I got nowhere else to be.

D5   A5
Right next door to Hell,

    E5   F#5
Feels like the walls are closing in on me.

Instrumental. ‖: E5 | E4 D4 E4 D4 E4 D4 | E5 | E4 D4 E4 :‖

                             Play 2 times

Verse 2

    B5   D5
My mama never really said much to me

    B5   A5 G5 A5
She was much too young and scared ta be

   B5   D5
Hell "Freud" might say that's what I need

   B5   A5 G5 A5
But all I really ever get is greed.

    B5   D5
An' most my friends they feel the same

    B5   A5   G5 A5
Hell we don't even have ourselves to blame,

    B5   D5
But times are hard and thrills are cheaper

    B5
As your arms get shorter

   A5   G5 A5
Your pockets get deeper.

Chorus 2

D5   A5
Right next door to Hell,

  E5   F#5
Why don't you write a letter to me.

    D5   A5
I said I'm right next door to hell,

  E5   F#5
An' so many eyes are on me.

cont.

D5   **A5**
Right next door to Hell,

       E5   **F#5**
I never thought this is where I'd be,

D5   **A5**
Right next door to Hell,

       E5   **F#5 F#5 F#5 F#5**
Thinkin' time'll stand still for me.

Instrumental 2. ‖: E | E | E | E |

   | C#m | C#m | C#m | C#m :‖ *Play 2 times*

   | B5 | B5 | B5 | B5 | B5 | B5 ‖

‖: E5 | E4 D4 E4 D4 E4 D4 | E5 | E4 D4 E4 :‖

                                Play 2 times

   | E5 F5 F#5 | E5 F#5 ‖

Outro

G   **A**
Not bad kids, just stupid ones,

         E
Yeah we thought we'd own the world

          E
An' gettin' used was havin' fun,

          G   **A**
I said we're not sad kids just lucid ones, yeah,

E   **E**
Flowin' through life not collectin' anyone.

G
So much out there,

        A
Still so much to see,

        E
Time's too much to handle,

        E
Time's too much for me,

        G
It drives me up the walls,

        A
Drives me out of my mind,

E
Can you tell me what this means——huh?

Raining Blood

Words & Music by
Jeffery Hanneman & Kerry King

Tune guitar down a semitone

Intro

(E5)

‖: Drums | Drums | Drums | Drums :‖

Play 4 times

riff A*

‖: E E E E* B♭ B♮ B♭ | F♯ B♭ A F♮ A G♯ :‖ *Play 4 times*

‖: E5 | E5 | E5 | E5 :‖

Play 4 times

(Faster)

| E5 | E5 | E5 | E5 ‖

‖: E5   B♭5 | E5   G5   B♭5 :‖ *Play 3 times*

Verse 1

 E5   C5 E5 D♯5 E5 B5 D5
Trapped in purgatory,
  E5   C5 E5 D♯5 E5 B5 D5
A lifeless object alive.
  E5   C5 E5 D♯5 E5 B5 D5
Awaiting reprisal,
 E5   C5 E5 D♯5   E5 B5 D5
Death will be their acquittance.
    E5   C5 E5 D♯5   E5 B5 D5
The sky is turning red,
  E5   C5 E5 D♯5   E5 B5 D5
Return to power draws near.
E5   C5 E5 D♯5   E5 B5 D5
Fall into me, the sky's crimson tears.
E5   C5 E5 D♯5 E5 B5 D5
Abolish the rules made of stone.

Interlude 1

‖: E5 | E5 | D♯5 | D♯5   A :‖

*to be played as single notes:

E = ⑥ open   F♯ = ⑤ 9fr
E* = ⑤ 7fr   A = ④ 7fr
B♭ = ④ 8fr   F♮ = ⑤ 8fr
B♮ = ④ 9fr   G♯ = ④ 6fr

Verse 2	**E5** **D#5 A5**
	Pierced from below, souls of our treacherous past.
	E5 **D#5 A5**
	Betrayed by many, now ornaments dripping above.

Interlude 2   ‖: **riff A** | **riff A** :‖

w/riff

Pre-chorus   Awaiting the hour of reprisal, your time slips away.

Interlude 3   ‖: **E5** | **E5** | **E5** | **E5** :‖ *Play 5 times*

Chorus

E5 G5 B5 E5   G5 B♭5   E5 A5 E5   G5 F#5
    Raining blood,
E5 G5 B5 E5   G5 B♭5   E5 A5 E5   G5 F#5
    From a lacerated sky.
E5 G5 B5 E5   G5 B♭5   E5 A5 E5   G5
Bleeding it's horror,
F#5 E5   G5   B5 E5 G5 B♭5
Creating my structure,
E5   A5 E5   G5 F#5 E5
Now I shall reign in blood!

w/double time feel

Outro   ‖: **E5** | **E5** | **E5** | **E5** :‖

| **G#5** | **G#5** |

‖: **E5** | **E5** | **E5** | **E5** :‖

Runnin' With The Devil

Words & Music by
Michael Anthony, David Lee Roth,
Edward Van Halen & Alex Van Halen

Tune guitar down a semitone

Intro　　‖: C D　　　| D Dsus4 Esus4 E　:‖

Play 4 times

Verse 1

A5 Groot A5　　G/A　　　　A6　　　A5
I　　live my life like there's no tomor - row

A5 Groot A5　　G/A A7　　Em
And　all I've got, I had to steal

A5 Groot A5　　G/A　　　A6　　　A5
Least I don't need to beg or bor - row

A5 Groot A5　　G/A A7　　Em
Yes　I'm liv - in' at a pace that kills.

Chorus 1

‖: C D
　　Ooh, yeah.

| D Dsus4 Esus4 E
　　　Runnin' with the

| C　　D　　|
De - vil.

| D Dsus4 Esus4 E　　　　　:‖
(2°) I'll tell you all about it.

Verse 2

A5 Groot A5　　　G/A　　　A6　　　A5
I　　found the simple life ain't so simple

A5 Groot A5　　　　G/A A7　　Em
When I jumped out, on that road

A5 Groot A5　　G/A　　A6　　　　A5
I　　got no love, no love you'd call re - al

A5 Groot A5　　　G/A　　A7　　Em
Ain't got nobo - dy, wait - in' at home.

Chorus 2　　As Chorus 1

| *Solo 1* | ‖ A5 | G5 | A5 | G5 D5 ‖ |

| *Intro* | ‖: C D | D Dsus4 Esus4 E :‖ |

Verse 3

A5 Groot A5   G/A
You know I,   I   found the sim - ple life

A6   A5
Weren't so simple, no

A5 Groot A5   G/A   A7   Em
      When I jumped out, on that road

A5 Groot A5   G/A   A6   A5
      Got no love, no love you'd call real

A5 Groot A5   G/A   A7   Em
      Got no - body, wait - in' at home.

Chorus 3   As Chorus 1

| *Solo 2* | ‖ A5 | G5 | A5 | G5 D5 ‖ |

Outro chorus

‖: C D	D Dsus4 Esus4 E	
(De - vil).		Runnin' with the
C D	D Dsus4 Esus4 E	:‖
De - vil.		Runnin' with the
C D	D Dsus4 Esus4 E N.C.	‖
De - vil.		

Sad But True

Words & Music by
James Hetfield & Lars Ulrich

Tune guitar down a tone

Intro	A5	B♭5	A5	B♭5			

| A5 | B♭5 | A5 | B♭5 N.C. |

riff A
| E5 DAB♭AGE | E5 DAB♭AGE | E5 DAB♭AGE |

| E5 DAB♭AGE | E5 DAB♭AGE | E5 DAB♭AGE |

| E5 DAB♭AGE | E5 DAD | D DAD |

| E5 DAB♭AGE | E5 DAB♭AGE |

Verse 1

E5   A4/E E5
Hey,   I'm your life,
       B♭5   E5
I'm the one who takes you there.
   A4/E E5
Hey,   I'm your life,
       B♭5 E5
I'm the one who cares.
   A4/E E5
They,   they betray,
      B♭5 E5
I'm your only true friend now.
   A4/E E5
They,   they'll betray,
      B♭5 E5
I'm forever there.

Chorus 1

    E5 A4/E F5   E5
I'm your dream,   make you real,

       Bb5 A5
I'm your eyes   when you must steal,

     G5   A5 G5   C5
I'm your pain   when you can't feel,

   E5
Sad but true.

E5   F5   E5
I'm your dream, mind astray,

       G5 A5
I'm your eyes while you're away,

         G5   C5
I'm your pain while you repay,

       E5
You know it's sad but true.

Link 1

  | riff A | riff A ‖: riff A :‖ *Play 4 times* | D A D |
                 Sad but true.

Verse 2

E5   A4/E E5
You,   you're my mask,

       Bb5 E5
You're my cover, my shelter.

    A4/E E5
You,   you're my mask

        Bb5   E5
You're the one who's blamed.

E5   A4/E E5
Do,   do my work,

      Bb5   E5
Do my dirty work, scapegoat.

    A4/E E5
Do,   do my deeds,

      Bb5   E5
For you're the one who's shamed.

Chorus 2   As Chorus 1

Link 2 | riff A | riff A | riff A ‖
                Sad but true.

Link 2 | A5 | B♭5 | A5 | B♭5 |

| A5 | B♭5 | A5 | B♭ N.C.‖

Solo ‖: riff A :‖ *Play 6 times*

| A5 | A5 | A5 | A5 ‖

Bridge
E5   F5   E5
I'm your dream,
         G5   A5
I'm your eyes,
         G5   C5
I'm your pain.
E5   F5   E5
I'm your dream,
         G5   A5
I'm your eyes,
         G5
I'm your pain.
C5 | E5 | E5 |
You know it's sad but true.

| E5 | E5 | D A D | D A D Fill ‖

Verse 3
E5   A4/E   E5
Hate,   I'm your hate,
                B♭5   E5
I'm your hate when you want love.
     A4/E   E5
Pay,   pay the price,
          B♭5   E5
Pay, for no - thing's fair.
     A4/E   E5
Hey,   I'm your life,
          B♭5   E5
I'm the one who took you here.
     A4/E   E5
Hey,   I'm your life,
          B♭5   E5
And I no long - er   care.

Chorus 3

E5   A4/E F5   E5
I'm your dream,   make you real,

        B♭5 A5
I'm your eyes when you must steal,

      G5   A5 G5   C5
I'm your pain when you can't feel,

      E5
Sad but true.

        F5   E5
I'm your truth, telling lies,

         G5   A5
I'm your rea - soned alibis,

        G5   C5
I'm in - side, open your eyes,

      E5
I'm you.

Outro

| riff A | riff A | riff A | D A D | E5 ‖

      Sad but true.

School's Out

Words & Music by
Alice Cooper, Michael Bruce, Dennis Dunaway,
Neal Smith & Glen Buxton

Intro	*Gtr. 1*	A/E	Em⁷	A/E	Em⁷	A/E	Em⁷	A/E	Em⁷
	Gtr. 2	N.C.		N.C.		E⁵		E⁵	

	Gtr. 1	A/E	Em⁷	A/E	Em⁷	A/E	Em⁷	A/E	Em⁷
	Gtr. 2	E⁷		E⁷		E⁷sus⁴		E⁷sus⁴	

	Gtr. 1	A/E	Em⁷	A/E	Em⁷	A/E	Em⁷	A/E	Em⁷
	Gtr. 2	A/E	Em⁷	A/E	Em⁷	A/E	Em⁷	A/E	Em⁷

Verse 1

        A/E   Em⁷   A/E
Well we got no choice,

Em⁷   A/E   Em⁷ A/E
   All the girls and boys

Em⁷   A/E   Em⁷ A/E
   Making all that noise

Em⁷   A/E   Em⁷ A/E
   'Cause they found new toys.

Em⁷   C
   Well we can't salute ya,

            D
Can't find a flag,

E♭
If that don't suit ya

That's a drag.

G5   B♭ C F5 G5
School's out for sum - mer.

     B♭ C F5 G5
School's out for ev - er.

       B♭ C F5 G5
School's been blown to pie - ces.

| A | G/A | F | F | |

C Cadd9#11 C Cadd9#11 C Cadd9#11 C Cadd9#11
No more pen - cils, no more bo - oks,

G/D D C/D D G/D D C/D D
No more tea - chers dir - ty looks yeah!

               x4

Link ‖: A/E   Em7 | A/E   Em7   :‖

     A/E   Em7   A/E
Verse 2 Well we got no class,

    Em7   A/E Em7   A/E
    And we got no principles,

    Em7   A/E Em7   A/E
    And we got no innocence,

    Em7   A/E   Em7 A/E   Em7
    We can't even think of a word that rhymes.

G5   B♭ C F5 G5
Chorus 2 School's out for sum - mer.

      B♭ C F5 G5
School's out for ev - er.

       F5   C
My school's been blown to pie - ces

C Cadd9#11 C Cadd9#11 C Cadd9#11 C Cadd9#11
No more pen - cils, no more bo - oks,

G/D D C/D D G/D D C/D D
No more tea - chers dir - ty looks!____

C Cadd9#11 C Cadd9#11 C Cadd9#11 C Cadd9#11
Out for sum - mer, out till fall,_____

G/D D C/D D G/D D C/D D
We might not go back at all. _____

G5   B♭ C F5 G5
School's out for ev - er.

     B♭ C F5 G5
School's out for sum - mer.

     B♭ C F5 G5
School's out with fev - er.

       F5 C
School's out com - plete - ly.

Run To The Hills

Words & Music by
Steve Harris

4 bars drum intro

Intro | A5 D | D A5 | C D | G5 A5 |

Verse 1

A5   D   A5
White man came across the sea
    C   D   G5   A5
He brought us pain and misery
            D   A5
He killed our tribes he killed our creed
    C   D   G5   A5
He took our game for his own need.
            D   A5
We fought him hard we fought him well
    C   D   G5   A5
Out on the plains we gave him hell
           D   A5
But many came too much for Cree
    C   D   G5   D
Oh will we ever be set free?

| D5 | D5 |

Verse 2

D5
Riding through dustclouds and barren wastes
C5   **G/B** **C5** **G/B**
Galloping hard on the plains
D5
Chasing the redskins back to their holes
C5   **G/B** **C5** **G/B**
Fighting them at their own game
A5   **C5**
Murder for freedom a stab in the back
F5   **D5**
Women and children and cowards attack.

Chorus 1

G5   **F**
  Run to the hills
C5   **(G/B)** **G5**
  Run for your lives.
         F
Run to the hills
C5   **(G/B)** **G5**
  Run for your lives.

Verse 3

D5
Soldier blue on the barren wastes
C5   **G/B** **C5** **G/B**
Hunting and killing's a game,
D5
Raping the women and wasting the men
C5   **G/B** **C5** **G/B**
The only good Indians are tame.
A5   **C5**
Selling them whisky and taking their gold
 F5   **D5**
Enslaving the young and destroying the old.

Chorus 2

G5   **F**
  Run to the hills
C5   **(G/B)** **G5**
  Run for your lives.
         F5
Run to the hills
C5   **(G/B)** **G5**
  Run for your lives.

| *Guitar Solo* | ‖: E5 | G5 | C5 | C5 | *x4* :‖ |

| | ‖: A5 | B5/A | C5/A | D5/A | *x4* :‖ |

Chorus 3

G5   F
  Run to the hills

C5   (G/B) G5
  Run for your lives.

         F
Run to the hills

C5   (G/B) G5
  Run for your lives.

G5   F
  Run to the hills

C5   (G/B) G5
  Run for your lives.

         F
Run to the hills

C5   G/B G5
  Run for your lives.

Slither

Words & Music by
Matt Sorum, Duff 'Rose' McKagan, David Kushner,
Saul Hudson & Scott Weilund

Tune 6th string to D

Intro ‖: D5 | Csus2/D | G/D | [1.] D5 :‖ [2.] D5 N.C. ‖

D5 riff _____ *Play 4 times*

‖: open 3fr 4fr open 6fr 7fr open 10fr | open 6fr 7fr open 5fr open 3fr :‖

⑥ _____ ⑥ _____

Hey!

Verse 1

D5 riff
When you look you see right through me
D5 riff
Cut the rope, fell to my knees
D5 riff   D5 riff
Fallen, broken every single time.

Verse 2

D5 riff
Always keep me under finger
D5 riff
That's the spot where you would see me
    D5 riff   D5 riff
Might see some type of pleasure in my mind.

Chorus 1

D5   Csus2
Yeah, here comes the water
        G/B   D5
It comes to wash away the sins of you and I
        D5 riff
This time you'll see.

‖: **D5 riff** | **D5 riff**   :‖ *Play 4 times*

Hey!

D5 riff

Verse 3   When you seek me you 'll destroy me

D5 riff

Rape my mind and smell the poppies

D5 riff   **D5 riff**

Born in blood in every single time.

D5 riff

Verse 4   Always keep me under finger

D5 riff

That 's the spot where you might linger

D5 riff   **D5 riff**

Might I see some type of pleasure in my mind.

D5   **Csus2**

Chorus 2   Yeah, here comes the water

                      G/B   **D5**

It comes to wash away the sins of you and I

                      D5

This time you'll see

                      Csus2

Like Holy water

                      G/B   **D5**

It only burns you faster than you'll ever dry

                              D5

This time with me.

| *Link 2* | | D5 | | Csus2/D | G/D | | D5 N.C. ||

| *Guitar solo* | ||: D5 | | D5 | | Csus2 | Csus2 |

| | G/B | | G/B Csus2 | D5 | | D5 | :||

D5 riff
Verse 5 When you look you see right through me
D5 riff
Cut the rope, I fell to my knees
D5 riff   **D5 riff**
 Fallen and broken every single time.

Chorus 3 As Chorus 1

Outro ||: **D5 riff** | **D5 riff** :|| *Play 3 times*
                                              Hey!

(D5)
| open 10fr 12fr open 9fr 10fr open 7fr |
⑥——————————

| open 6fr 7fr open 5fr open 3fr 4fr | open N.C. ||
⑥——————————

145

Souls Of Black

Words & Music by
Alex Skolnick, Luciano Clemente, Billy Charles,
Gregory Christian & Eric Petersen

Intro
| E5 | G5 F#5 | E5 | G5 F#5 ‖
‖: E5 | E5 | E5 | E5 :‖ *Play 4 times*
| B♭5 | | B♭5 A5 N.C. ‖

Riff 1

| E5 G5 A5 G5 | E5 G5 B♭5 C#5 D5 |

D 10fr ⑥   C# 9fr ⑥   C 8fr ⑥   B♭ 6fr ⑥

| E5 G5 B♭5 ♩ | ♩. ♪♩ ♩ |

| E5 G5 A5 G5 | E5 G5 B♭5 C#5 D5 |

D 10fr ⑥   C# 9fr ⑥   E open ⑥

| E5 G5 B♭5 ♩ | ♩. ♪♪♪ D5 ‖

Verse 1

E5w/riff 1
Oh, can't you see

That in the world we live in

Political lies

Are just corporate decisions

They'll take away

All the hopes, not their promises

They'll put an end to this

Land of the living.

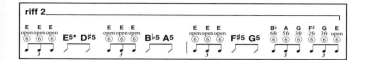

Chorus 1

E5w/riff 1
Look at the lost souls

They seem so black

Look at the lost souls
G5
Souls of black.

Link 1

| E5 | E5 | E5 | E5 |

| E5 | E5 | E5 | E5 N.C. B♭5 A5 G5 ‖

Verse 2

E5w/riff 1
They got control

Of the heart of a nation

Their social tribes

Seem so graciously

As time goes by

'Cause time as you can see

Will slowly die now for you and me.

Chorus 2

E5w/riff 2
Look at the lost souls

They seem so black

Look at the lost souls
G5 | **A5**   **B♭5 A5 G5** |
Souls of black.

Solo ‖: E5 G5 B♭5 | E5 |E5 G5 B♭5 | B5 |

| E5 G5 F♯5 | C5 |D5 D♯5 | E5   :‖

| B♭5 | B♭5 N.C.   ‖

Verse 3
E5 w/riff 1
So put an end

To this idolization

Antagonizing so commonly

Open your eyes

'Cause the lie's there so plain to see

Life goes on

There's no guarantees.

Chorus 3
E5 w/riff 2
Look at the lost souls

They seem so black

Look at the lost souls
G5
Souls of black.

Outro
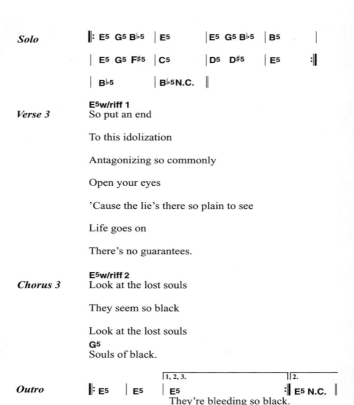
‖: E5 | E5 | E5 :‖ E5 N.C. ‖

1, 2, 3.   2.

They're bleeding so black.

148

The Spirit Of Radio

Words by Neil Peart
Music by Geddy Lee & Alex Lifeson

Intro

N.C.	N.C.	E	(E)	(E)	(E)
E	(E)	(E)	E	A	E
A	E	A	E	A	E
Bsus⁴	E/G♯	A B	E	
Bsus⁴	E/G♯	A C♯m B

Verse 1

    E   Bsus⁴
Begin the day with a friendly voice,
      E/G♯   A   B
A companion, unobtrusive,
E   Bsus⁴
Plays that song that's so elusive
        E/G♯   A   B
And the magic music makes your   morning mood.

Link 1

| E | Bsus⁴ | E/G♯ | A   C♯m B |

Verse 2

E   Bsus⁴
Off on your way, hit the   open road,
      E/G♯   A   B
There is magic at your fingers,
E   B add⁴
   For the Spirit ever lingers,
      E/G♯   A   B
Undemanding contact in your happy solitude.

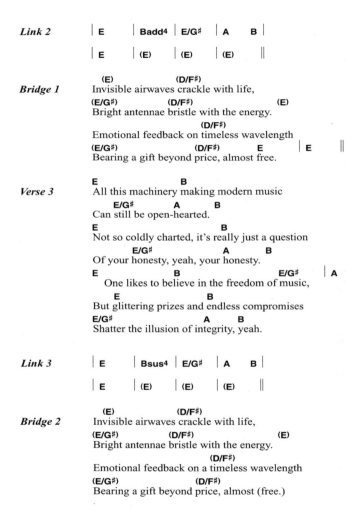

Link 2 | E | Badd4 | E/G♯ | A   B |
| E | (E) | (E) | (E) ‖

Bridge 1

(E)   (D/F♯)
Invisible airwaves crackle with life,
(E/G♯)   (D/F♯)   (E)
Bright antennae bristle with the energy.
                              (D/F♯)
Emotional feedback on timeless wavelength
(E/G♯)   (D/F♯)   E | E   ‖
Bearing a gift beyond price, almost free.

Verse 3

E   B
All this machinery making modern music
     E/G♯   A   B
Can still be open-hearted.
E   B
Not so coldly charted, it's really just a question
     E/G♯   A   B
Of your honesty, yeah, your honesty.
E   B   E/G♯ | A   B
   One likes to believe in the freedom of music,
     E   B
But glittering prizes and endless compromises
E/G♯   A   B
Shatter the illusion of integrity, yeah.

Link 3 | E | Bsus4 | E/G♯ | A   B |
| E | (E) | (E) | (E) ‖

Bridge 2

(E)   (D/F♯)
Invisible airwaves crackle with life,
(E/G♯)   (D/F♯)   (E)
Bright antennae bristle with the energy.
                              (D/F♯)
Emotional feedback on a timeless wavelength
(E/G♯)   (D/F♯)
Bearing a gift beyond price, almost (free.)

Link 4

| E | E | D/F♯ | D/F♯ |
free.

| E/G♯ | E/G♯ | D/F♯ | D/F♯ |

| E | E | D/F♯ | D/F♯ |

| E/G♯ | E/G♯ | D/F♯ | D/F♯ |

‖: E | Bsus⁴ | E/G♯ | A   B :‖ E | (E) | N.C |

‖: E | A | E | A :‖ E | A   B ‖

Verse 4

    E
For the words of the profits
   A   B   E   A
Were written on the studio wall,
B   E
Concert hall,

| A | E | A | E | A   B |

   E   A   B E   A
And echoes with the sound   of salesmen.
   E   A
Of salesmen,   of (salesmen.)

Guitar solo

| E | A | E | A |
salesmen.

‖: E | A | E | A :‖

Coda

| E | A | E | A |

| E | A | (E) | (E) | N.C. | E ‖

Stacked Actors

Words & Music by
Dave Grohl, Taylor Hawkins & Nate Mendel

Intro

‖: (A) | (G) | (F) | (D) :‖

‖: A | G | F | D :‖

‖: Am⁷ A¹³ | Am⁷ A¹³ |

| Am⁷ A¹³ | Am⁷ A¹³ A⁷♭5 A¹³ :‖

Verse 1

Am⁷   A¹³   Am⁷   A¹³
  Oh mirror mirror, you're coming in clear,

    Am⁷   A¹³   Am⁷ A¹³ A⁷♭5 A¹³
I'm finally somewhere   in between.

Am⁷   A¹³   Am⁷   A¹³
  I'm impressed,what a beautiful chest,

    Am⁷   A¹³   Am⁷ A¹³ A⁷♭5 A¹³
I never meant to make a big scene.

Am⁷   A¹³   Am⁷   A¹³
  Will you resign to the latest design?

        Am⁷
You look so messy when you

   A¹³   Am⁷ A¹³ A⁷♭5 A¹³
Dress up in dreams.

Am⁷   A¹³   Am⁷   A¹³
  One more for hire or a wonderful liar?

Am⁷   A¹³   Am⁷ A¹³ A⁷♭5 A¹³
I think it's time we all should come clean.

Pre-chorus 1

    Am⁷
Stack dead actors, stacked to the rafters,

Line up the bastards, all I want is the truth.

Chorus 1

    A   G
Hey, hey now, can you fake it?

    F   D
Can you make it look like we want?

    A   G
Hey, hey now, can you take it?

    F   D
And we cry when they all die blonde.

Link 1   ‖: **Am7** **A13** | **Am7** **A13** |

| **Am7** **A13** | **Am7** **A13** **A7♭5** **A13** :‖

Verse 2

   Am7   **A13**   **Am7**
   God bless,   what a sensitive mess,

A13   **Am7**
Yeah, but things aren't

    A13   **Am7** **A13** **A7♭5** **A13**
always what they seem.

Am7   **A13**   **Am7**   **A13**
   Your teary eyes,   your famous disguise,

Am7   **A13**   **Am7** **A13** **A7♭5** **A13**
Never knowing who to believe.

Am7   **A13**   **Am7**
   See through, yeah but what do you do

A13   **Am7**
   When you're just another

   A13   **Am7**   **A13** **A7♭5** **A13**
ancient drag queen?

Pre-chorus 2

Am7
   Stack dead actors, stacked to the rafters,

Line up the bastards, all I want is the truth.

Chorus 2

    A   **G**
Hey, hey now, can you fake it?

       F   **D**
Can you make it look like we want?

    A   **G**
Hey, hey now, can you take it?

    F   **D**
And we cry when they all die blonde.

Chorus 3

  A   **G**
Stack dead actors, stacked to the rafters;

  F   **D**
Line up all the bastards, all I want is the truth.

A   **G**
Stack dead actors, stacked to the rafters;

F
Line up all the bastards.

    D
And we cry when they all die (blonde.)

Link 2 | **(A)** | **(A)** | **(A)** | **(E♭)** ‖
    blonde.

Guitar solo   ‖: A | A | A | E♭   :‖

Play 4 times

               A   **G**

Chorus 4   Hey, hey now, can you fake it?

               F   **D**

Can you make it look like we want?

               A   **G**

Hey, hey now, can you take it?

               F   **D**

And we cry when they all die blonde.

     A   **G**

Chorus 5   Stack dead actors, stacked to the rafters,

      F   **D**

Line up all the bastards, all I want is the truth.

     A   **G**

Stack dead actors, stacked to the rafters,

     F

Line up the bastards.

               D   **N.C.**

And we cry when they all die (blonde.)

Coda | Am⁷ A¹³ | Am⁷ A¹³ | Am⁷ A¹³ | Am⁷ A¹³ |

blonde.

‖: Am⁷ A¹³ | Am⁷ A¹³ | Am⁷ A¹³ | Am⁷ A¹³ :‖

| Am⁷   ‖

Stockholm Syndrome

Words & Music by
Matthew Bellamy, Chris Wolstenholme & Dominic Howard

Tune 6th string to D

Intro

Riff 1

| 1. |

|: D E♭ D C D D E♭ D C D | D E♭ D C D D E♭ F♯ G F♯:|
open 13fr 12fr 10fr 12fr open 13fr 12fr 10fr 12fr   open 13fr 12fr 10fr open 13fr 16fr 17fr 16fr
⑥

| 2. |

| **N.C.** ‖

‖: **Riff 1** | **(Riff 1)**   :‖ *Play 4 times*

Verse 1

     Doct D(7)   **D(6)**   **D(♭6)**
I won't stand in your way,——

        Doct A/E F5   **D/F♯**
Let your ha - tred grow.——

       Gm
And she'll scream,

      Dm/F
And she'll shout,

      Em7 E♭sus2
And she'll pray...——

     A7sus4
And she had a name,

     A
Yeah, she had a name.

Verse 2

        Doct D(7)   D(6) D(♭6)
And I won't hold you back,——

        Doct A/E F5 D/F♯
Let your an - ger rise.——

    Gm
And we'll fly,

    Dm/F
And we'll fall,

    Em7 E♭sus2
And we'll burn...——

    A7sus4
No one will recall,

    A   **G5 F♯5** | **F5** | **F5** | **F5** | **F5** ‖
No one will recall.

Bridge 1

F5   **A/E**   **Dm**
This is the last time I'll a - bandon you,

        F5   **A/E**   **Dm**   **B♭5**
And this is— the last time I'll for - get you,——

        F5 A♭5 | **A5 C5 D♭5** ‖
I wish I could.

Link

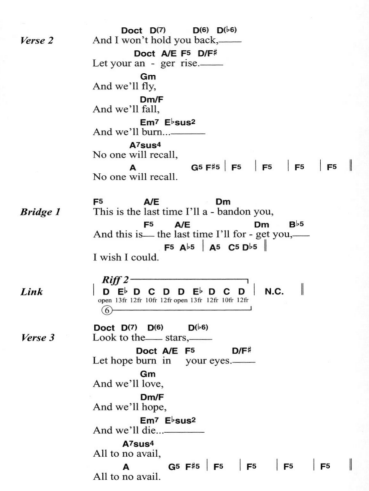

Verse 3

Doct D(7) D(6)   **D(♭6)**
Look to the—— stars,——

        Doct A/E F5   **D/F♯**
Let hope burn in   your eyes.——

    Gm
And we'll love,

    Dm/F
And we'll hope,

    Em7 E♭sus2
And we'll die...——

    A7sus4
All to no avail,

    A   **G5 F♯5** | **F5** | **F5** | **F5** | **F5** ‖
All to no avail.

Bridge 2   As Bridge 1

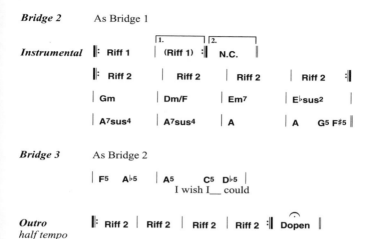

Instrumental ‖: Riff 1 | (Riff 1) :‖ N.C. ‖

‖: Riff 2 | Riff 2 | Riff 2 | Riff 2 :‖

| Gm | Dm/F | Em7 | E♭sus2 |

| A7sus4 | A7sus4 | A | A   G5 F♯5 ‖

Bridge 3   As Bridge 2

| F5   A♭5 | A5   C5   D♭5 |
            I wish I__ could

Outro   ‖: Riff 2 | Riff 2 | Riff 2 | Riff 2 :‖ D open ‖
half tempo

157

Stargazer

Words & Music by
Ritchie Blackmore & Ronnie Dio

Intro　　　Drums | E5 　　| E5　D/E | E5 　　　|

　　　　　 | E5 　 G5 | (G5) 　| G5 A5 ‖

Verse 1

E5　　　　　　　　　　　　　　　　　　　　　 D/E
　　High noon, oh, I'd sell my soul for water

E5　　　　　　　　　　　　　　　　　　 D/E
　　Nine years worth of breaking my back

E5　　　　　　　　　　　　　　　　　　　　　　 D/E
　　There's no sun in the shadow of the wizard

E5　　　　　　　　　　　　　　　　　　 N.C.
See how he glides, why he's lighter than air.

Pre-chorus 1

F♯5　G5　A5　C5　B5
Oh, I　see his face

B5
Where is your star?

C5　　　B5　　　　　　　　　 C5　B5
　　Is it far, is it far, is it far?

　　　　　　　　　　　　　　 C5　B5
When do we leave?

　　　　　　　　 | G5　A5 C5　 B5 |
I believe, yes, I believe.

Chorus 1

A5
In the heat and the rain with whips and chains

G5
Just to see him fly so many died

A5
We built a tower of stone with our flesh and bone

G5
Just to see him fly, don't know why

| G5 D5　G5 C5　D5 | (D5) 　　|

N.C.　　　　　　　　 E5
Now where do we go?————

Verse 2

E5   D/E
Hot wind moving fast across the desert

E5   D/E
We feel that our time has arrived

E5   D/E
The world spins while we put his wing together

E5   N.C.
A tower of stone to take him straight to the sky.

Pre-chorus 2

F#5   G5 A5 C5 B5
Oh, I   see his face

B5
Where is your star?

C5   B5   C5 B5
It is far, is it far, is it far?

                 C5 B5
When do we leave? Yeah!

         | G5 A5 C5   B5 |
I believe, I believe.

Chorus 2

A5
In the heat and the rain with whips and chains

G5
Just to see him fly so many died

A5
We built a tower of stone with our flesh and bone

G5
Just to see him fly, don't know why

| G5 D5 G5 C5 D5 | (D5) |

N.C.   B5
Now where do we go?_____

Solo

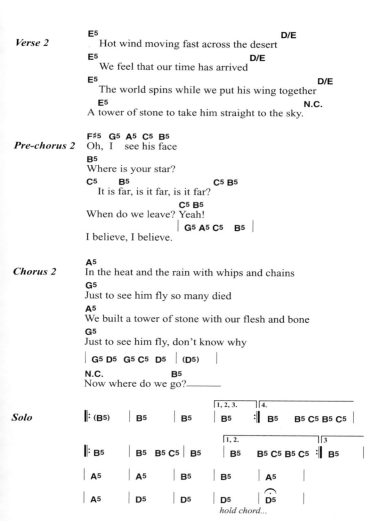

hold chord...

Verse 2

E5   **D/E**
All eyes see the figure of the wizard

E5   **D/E**
As he climbs to the top of the world

E5   **D/E**
No sound as he falls instead of rising

E5   **N.C.**
Time standing still then there's blood on the sand.

Pre-chorus 3

F♯5   G5 A5   C5 B5
Oh, I   see his face

B5
Where was your star?

**   C5 B5**
Was it far, was it far?

**   C5 B5**
When did we leave?

                                              | **G5 A5 C5   B5** |
We believe, we believe, we believe.

Chorus 3

A5
In the heat and rain with whips and chains

G5
To see him fly so many died

A5
We built a tower of stone with our flesh and bone

G5
To see him fly.

**   A5**
But why, it don't rain with all our chains

G5
Did so many die just to see him fly

A5
Look at my flesh and bone

**   G5**
Now look, look, look, look, look at this tower of stone.

A5
I see a rainbow rising...

G5
Look there on the horizon

**   A5**
And I'm coming home, I'm coming home

G5
I'm coming home.

A5
Time is standing still, he gave me back my will

G5
Oh, oh, oh, oh

A5
Going home, I'm going home

G5
My eyes are bleeding and my heart is weeping.

A5
We still hope, we still hope

G5
Oh.———

A5
Take me back, he gave me back my will

G5
Oh, oh, oh, oh.

A5
Going home, I'm going home

G5
My eyes are bleeding and my heart is weeping

A5
We still hope, we still hope

G5
Oh.———

A5
Take me back, take me back

G5
Back to my home, oh, oh... *to fade*

Strutter

Words & Music by
Paul Stanley & Gene Simmons

Intro

| B♭ | G♭ | D♭ | A♭ |

| B♭ | G♭ | D♭ | D♭   ‖

Verse 1

    B♭   G♭   D♭   D♭sus⁴ D♭
I know a thing or two about her,
    B♭   G♭   D♭   A♭
I know she'll only make you cry.
    B♭   G♭   D♭   D♭sus⁴ D♭
She'll let you walk the street beside her,
    B♭   G♭   D♭   A♭
But when she wants, she'll pass you by.

Chorus 1

    B♭5   G♭5
Everybody says she's looking good,
    B♭5   G♭5
And the lady knows it's understood.
    A♭5 B♭5 A♭5 B5♭ A♭5 B♭5
Strutter.
    D♭5 E♭5 D♭5 B♭5 A♭5 F5

Interlude

| A♭5   B♭5 | A♭5   B♭5   A♭5   B♭5 ‖

| D♭5   E♭5 | G♭5   C♭5   D♭5   A♭5 ‖

Verse 2

    B♭   G♭   D♭   D♭sus⁴ D♭
She wears her satins like a lady
    B♭   G♭   D♭   A♭
She gets her way like a child.
    B♭   G♭   D♭   D♭sus⁴ D♭
You take her home and she says "maybe, baby"
    B♭   G♭   D♭   A♭
She takes you down and drives you wild.

Chorus 2

B♭5   G♭5
Everybody says she is looking good,
B♭5   G♭5
And the lady knows it's understood.

Solo

‖: A♭5 B♭5 | A♭5 B♭5 A♭5 B♭5 |
   Strutter.
| D♭5 E♭5 | D♭5 B♭5 A♭5 F5 :‖

| A♭5 B♭5 | A♭5 B♭5 A♭5 B♭5 |

| D♭5 E♭5 | G♭5 C♭5 D♭5 A♭5 ‖

Verse 3

B♭   G♭   D♭   D♭sus4 D♭
I know a thing or two about her,
B♭   G♭   D♭   A♭
I know she'll only make you cry.
B♭   G♭   D♭   D♭sus4 D♭
She'll let you walk the street beside her,
B♭   G♭   D♭   A♭
But when she wants, she'll pass you by.

Chorus 3

B♭5   G♭5
Everybody says she's looking good,
B♭5   G♭5
And the lady knows it's understood.

‖: A♭5 B♭5   A♭5 B5♭ A♭5 B♭5
Strutter.
D♭5 E♭5   D♭5 B♭5 A♭5 F5 :‖

Strutter.
| A♭5 B♭5 | A♭5 B♭5 A♭5 B♭5 |

| D♭5 E♭5 | G♭5 C♭5 D♭5 A♭5 | B♭5 ‖

Take A Look Around
(Theme from "M:I-2")

Words by Fred Durst
Music by Lalo Schifrin

Tune guitar down a semitone

Intro
‖: **(Em)**   **(G)** | **(Em)**   **(D)** | **(Em)**   **(G)** | **(Em)**   **(D)** :‖

‖: **(Em)** | **(G)** | **(C)** | **(D)**   :‖

Play 3 times

Verse 1
Em
    All the teachin' in the world today,
    G
All the little girls filling up the world today.
    C
With the good comes the bad, the bad comes to good,
      D
But I'm-a gonna live my life like I should.
Em   **G**
    Now all the critics wanna hit it. This hit? How we did it,
                            C
Just because they don't get it, but I'll stay fitted,
                        D
New era committed, now this red cap gets a rap from his critics

Pre-chorus
      Em   **G**
    Do we always gotta cry, do we always gotta live inside a lie?
C
Life's just a blast, 'cause it's movin' really fast,
      D
You better stay on top or life'll kick you in the ass.

Verse 1
      Em
    Follow me into a solo,
            G
Remember that kid, so what you wanna do?
        C
And where you gonna run when you're starin' down the cable
      D
Of my mic pointed at your grill like a gun?

cont.

Em   **G**
        Limp Bizkit is rockin' the set, it's like Russian roulette

        When you're placin' your bet,
            C
        So don't be upset when you're broke and you're done,
                D
        'Cause I'm gonna be the one till I jet.

Chorus 1
        E5   **G A**
        I know why you wanna hate me,
        E5   **D5 D♯5**
        I know why you wanna hate me,
        E5   **G A**
        I know why you wanna hate me,
                E5   **D5   D♯5**
        'Cause hate is all the world has even seen late - ly.
        E5   **G A**
        I know why you wanna hate me,
        E5   **D5 D♯5**
        I know why you wanna hate me,
        E5   **G A**
        Now I know why you wanna hate me,
                E5   **D5   D♯5**
        'Cause hate is all the world has even seen late - ly.

        | **E5**   **G A** | **E5**   **D5 D♯5** |
        E5   **G A**
        And now you wanna hate me,
                E5   **D5   D♯5**
        'Cause hate is all the world has even seen late - ly.

        | **E5**   **G A** | **E5**   **D5 D♯5** |
        E5   **G A**
        Now you wanna hate me,
                E5   **D5   D♯5**
        'Cause hate is all the world has even seen late - ly.

Link | **Em** | **G** | **C** | **D** ||

Verse 3

    Em
Does anybody really know the secret

   G
Or the combination for this life

And where they keep it?

 C
  It's kinda sad when you don't know the meanin'

D
But everything happens for a reason.

Em
I don't even know what I should say,

       G
'Cause I'm an idiot, a loser, a microphone abuser.

C
  I analyse every second I exist,

D
Beatin' up my mind every second with my fist.

Pre-chorus

 Em
  And everybody wanna run,

   G
Everybody wanna hide from the gun,

 C
You can take a ride through this life if you want

     D
 But you can't take the edge off the knife, no sir.

Em   **G**
  And now you want your money back but you're denied,

'Cause your brains fried from the sack

C
  And there ain't nothin' I can do,

    D
'Cause life is a lesson,

You learn it when you're through.

Chorus 2

E5   **G A**
  I know why you wanna hate me,

E5   **D5 D♯5**
  I know why you wanna hate me,

E5   **G A**
  I know why you wanna hate me,

     E5   **D5**   **D♯5**
'Cause hate is all the world has even seen late - ly.

    E5   **G A**
     I know why you wanna hate me,
    E5   **D5 D#5**
 I know why you wanna hate me,
    E5   **G A**
   Now I know why you wanna hate me,
         E5   **D5**   **D#5**
'Cause hate is all the world has even seen late - ly.

 | **E5**   **G A** | **E5**   **D5 D#5** |
    E5   **G A**
   Now you wanna hate me,
       E5   **D5**   **D#5**
'Cause hate is all the world has even seen late - ly.

 | **E5**   **G A** | **E5**   **D5 D#5** |
    E5   **G A**
   Now you wanna hate me,
       E5   **D5**   **D#5**
'Cause hate is all the world has even seen late - ly.

Bridge   ‖: **E5**   **G A** | **E5**   **D5 D#5** :‖   *Play 6 times*

             ‖: **Em** | **G** | **C** | **D**   :‖   *Play 4 times*
               Now   I   know   why.

             E5   **G A**
Chorus 3 Now I know why you wanna hate me,
             E5   **D5 D#5**
            Now I know why you wanna hate me,
             E5   **G A**
            Now I know why you wanna hate me,
                   E5   **D5**   **D#5** **E5**
            'Cause hate is all the world has even seen late - ly,
    G A   **E5**   **D5**   **D#5** **E5**
          'Cause hate is all the world has even seen late - ly,
    G A   **E5**   **D5**   **D#5**
          'Cause hate is all the world has even seen late - ly.

Coda   ‖: **Em** | **G** | **C** | **D**   :‖   *Repeat and fade*

These Boots
Are Made For Walking

Words & Music by
Lee Hazlewood

Intro

‖: E | E | E | E   :‖

Play 4 times

‖: E5 | E5 | E5 | E5 |

| E5 G5 E5 D5 | E5 G5 E5 D5 | E5 G5 E5 D5 | E5 G5 E5 D5 :‖

| Esus2 | Esus2 | Esus2 | Esus2   ‖

w/double time feel

‖: Em7 | E5   :‖   *Play 4 times*

**
| E5 | E5 | E5 | E5 |

| E5 | E5   D5 | E5 | E5   D5 ‖

Verse 1

     E5   D5
You keep saying you got something for me.
     E5   D5
Something you call love, but I call sex.
     A5   C5 D5
You've been kissing when you ought-to-be-a-screwing,
     E5
And now someone else can kiss your ass.

Chorus 1

         G5   E5
These boots are made for walking,
        G5   E5
And that's just what they'll do.
      G5   E5
One of these days these boots
                N.C
Are gonna walk all over you.

***Gtrs descend chromatically
from: E = ⑥ 12fr**

Solo 1

| E5 | E5 | E5 | E5 |

| E5 G5 E5 D5 | E5 G5 E5 D5 | E5 G5 E5 D5 | E5 G5 E5 D5 |

| E5 | E5 | E5 | E5 |

| E5 | E5 ||

Verse 2

E5   D5
You been lying and there ain't no believing.
E5   D5
And you keep samin' when you ought to not bet.
A5   C5 D5
You been staying when you ought-to-be-a-leaving,
E5
Now what's right is right but you ain't been right yet.

Chorus 1   As Chorus 1

Solo 2

| E5 | E5 | E5 | E5 |

| E5 | E5 ||: E5 | E5 D5 :||

Verse 3

E5   D5
You keep dressing ways you shouldn't be dressing.
E5   D5
And you keep thinking that you'll never get burned, ha!
A5   C5 D5
I just found me a brand new box spring matress,
E5
What you know, bitch, you got a lot to learn.

Chorus 3   As Chorus 1

Solo 2

| E5 | E5 | E5 | E5 |

| E5 | E5 ||

Outro

      E5   E5 D5
||: Are you ready boots? :|| *Play 3 times*

||: E5 :|| *Play 3 times*

Territory

Words & Music by
Andreas Kisser, Max Cavalera, Igor Cavalera & J. Paulo

Tune Guitar D A D G B E

Intro

Drums
4

| D5 C#5 | D5 C#5 | D5 C#5 | D5 C#5 | D5 C#5 | D5 C#5 | D5 C#5 | D5 C#5 |

| D5 | D5 | D5 | D5 |

| Ebroot | Ebroot | Ebroot | Ebroot |

| D5 | (D5) | Drums | Drums |

hold chord

riff 2

| F#5 Eb5 Eb5 F5 Eb5 Eb5 | D5 Dm | F#5 Eb5 Eb5 F5 Eb5 Eb5 | G5 |

riff 1

G	E	Eb	Eb	G	E	Eb	Eb
5fr	2fr	1fr	1fr	5fr	2fr	1fr	1fr
6	6	6	6	6	6	6	6

w/riff 1

Verse 1
Unknown man

Speaks to the world

Sucking your trust

A trap in every world.

Chorus 1

w/riff 2
War for territory

War for territory.

Link 1

| Eᵇroot | Eᵇroot | Eᵇroot | Eᵇroot ‖

Verse 2

w/riff 1
Choice control

Behind propaganda

Poor information

To manage your anger.

Chorus 2

w/riff 2
War for territory

War for territory.

Link 2

| D5 | (D5) | (D5) | (D5) ‖

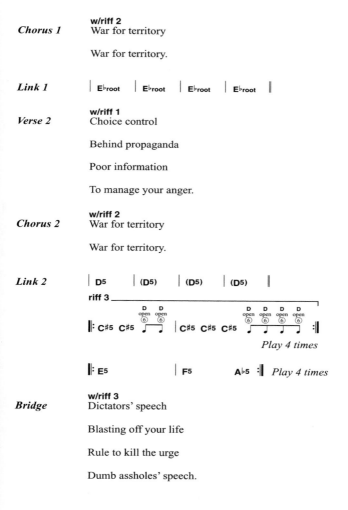

Play 4 times

‖: E5 | F5 | Aᵇ5 :‖ *Play 4 times*

Bridge

w/riff 3
Dictators' speech

Blasting off your life

Rule to kill the urge

Dumb assholes' speech.

‖: E♭root │ E♭root │ E♭root │ E♭root C#5 D5 E♭5 :‖

‖: D5 B5 │ E♭5 C5 │ D5 B5 │ D5 │ :‖

│ E♭root │ E♭root │ E♭root │ E♭root C#5 D5 E♭5 ‖

‖: D5 C#5 │ D5 C#5 │ D5 C#5 │ D5 C#5 :‖

‖: C#5 │ C#5 │ C#5 │ C#5 :‖

│ N.C. (Drums) │ (Drums) ‖

w/riff 1

Verse 3   Years of fighting

Teaching my son

To believe in that man

Racist human being

Racist ground will live

Shame and regret

Of the pride

You've once possessed.

w/riff 2

Chorus 3   War for territory

⌢
..
Dm

War for territory.

Outro   ‖: E♭root │ E♭root │ E♭root │ E♭root :‖

Toxicity

Words by Serj Tankian
Music by Daron Malakian & Shavo Odadjian

Tune guitar: C G C F A D

Intro

‖: C5 | C5 | E♭5 | E♭5 :‖

‖: C5 | E♭5 D5 C5 D5 C5 | A♭5 | G5 :‖

Riff 1

| E♭5 D5 C5 E♭5 D5 C5 | ℅ | ℅ | ℅ | A♭5 | G5 |

| C5 | E♭5 D5 C5 D5 C5 | A♭5 | G5 ‖

‖: C5 | C5 | E♭5 | E♭5 :‖

Verse 1

C5   E♭5
Conversion software version seven point '0',

C5   E♭5
Looking at life through the eyes of a tyre hub.

C5   E♭5
Eating seeds as a pastime activity,

C5   E♭5
The toxicity of our city, of our city.

Chorus 1

C5   E♭5 D5 C5 D5 C5
You, what do you own the world?

            A♭5   G5
How do you own disorder, disorder.

C5   E♭5 D5 C5 D5 C5
Now, somewhere between the sacred silence,

A♭5   G5
Sacred silence and sleep.

Riff 1   A♭5   G5
Somewhere, between the sacred silence and sleep,

C5   E♭5 D5 C5 D5 C5   A♭5   G5
Disorder, disorder,   disor - der.

| *Link* | ‖: C5 | | C5 | | E♭5 | | E♭5 | :‖ |

Verse 2

C5   E♭5
More wood for their fires, loud neighbours.

C5   E♭5
Flashlight reveries caught in the headlights of a truck.

C5   E♭5
Eating seeds as a pastime activity,

C5   E♭5
The toxicity of our city, of our city.

Chorus 2   As Chorus 1

Interlude

N.C.
| (C5) | ∕ | ∕ | ∕ ‖

| C5   E♭5 D5 C5 D5 |

| E♭5 D5 C5 C5 C5 C5 E♭5 D5 C5 C5 C5 C5 |

| ∕ | ∕ | C5 E♭5 D5 C5 D5 | ∕ |

| ∕ | ∕ | E♭5 D5 C5 C5 C5 C5 E♭5 D5 C5 C5 C5 C5 |

| ∕ | ∕ | ∕ |

Chorus 3

C5   E♭5 D5 C5 D5 C5
You, what do you own the world?

        A♭5   G5
How do you own disorder, disorder.

C5   E♭5 D5 C5 D5 C5
Now, somewhere between the sacred silence,

A♭5   G5
Sacred silence and sleep.

Riff 1   A♭5   G5
Somewhere, between the sacred silence and sleep,

C5   E♭5 D5 C5 D5 C5
Disorder, disorder,

  A♭5 G5 | E♭5 D5 C5 C5 C5 C5

E♭5 D5 C5 C5 C5 C5 | ⟋ | ⟋ | ⟋ |

Disor - der.

Outro

C5   E♭5 C5 D5
When I became the sun,

 C5   E♭5 C5 D5
I shone life into the man's hearts.

C5   E♭5 C5 D5
When I became the sun,

 C5   E♭5 C5 D5
I shone life into the man's hearts.

175

The Trooper

Words & Music by
Steve Harris

Intro   ‖: E5 :‖ *Play 8 times*

‖: E5 | D5 G5 D5 E5 | E5 | D5 G5 D5 C5 |

| C5 | D5 G5 D5 E5 | E5 | D5 G5 D5 E5 :‖

Verse 1

N.C   D5 G5 D5 E5
You'll take my life but I'll take yours too.
N.C   D5 G5 D5 C5
You'll fire your musket but I'll run you through.
N.C   D5 G5 D5 E5
So when you're waiting for the next attack,
              D5 G5 D5 E5
You'd better stand there's no turning back.

Verse 2

(E5)   D5 G5 D5 E5
The bugle sounds and the charge begins,
          D5 G5 D5 C5
But on this battlefield no one wins.
          D5 G5 D5 E5
The smell of acrid smoke and horse's breath,
        D5
As I plunge on into certain death.

Link 1

D5   E5   D5   E5   D5 G5 D5 E5
Oh.   Oh.

Interlude

| E5 | D5G5D5E5 | E5 | D5G5D5C5 |

| C5 | C5F5C5D5 | D5 | D5G5D5E5 |

| E5 | D5G5D5E5 | E5 | D5G5D5E5 |

| E5 | C5F5C5D5 | D5 | D5G5E5 ‖

Verse 3

E5   D5 G5 D5 E5

The horse, he sweats with fear, we break to run,

D5 G5 D5 C5

The mighty roar of the Russian guns.

D5 G5 D5 E5

And as we race towards the human wall,

D5 G5 D5 E5

The screams of pain as my comrades fall.

Verse 4

(E5)   D5 G5 D5 E5

We hurdle bodies that lay on the ground,

D5 G5 D5 C5

And the Russians fire another round.

D5 G5 D5 E5

We get so near yet so far away,

We won't live to fight another day.

Link 2   As link 1

Solo

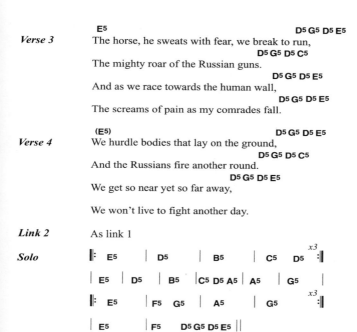

	E5 **D5 G5 D5 E5**
Verse 3	We get so close, near enough to fight,
	D5 G5 D5 C5
	When a Russian gets me in his sights.
	D5 G5 D5 E5
	He pulls the trigger and I feel the blow,
	D5 G5 D5 E5
	A burst of rounds take my horse below.

E5   **D5 G5 D5 E5**

Verse 3   We get so close, near enough to fight,

                                           D5 G5 D5 C5

When a Russian gets me in his sights.

                                              D5 G5 D5 E5

He pulls the trigger and I feel the blow,

                                                 D5 G5 D5 E5

A burst of rounds take my horse below.

(E5)   **D5 G5 D5 E5**

Verse 4   And I lay there gazing at the sky,

                                           D5 G5 D5 C5

My body's numb and my throat is dry.

                                      D5 G5 D5 E5

And as I lay, forgotten and alone,

                                           D5 G5 D5 E5

Without a tear I draw my parting groan.

Link 3   As link 2

Outro   ‖:   **E**   :‖   *Play 7 times*

         | **E**   **D5**   **E5**   ‖

Victim Of Changes

Words & Music by
Kenneth Downing, Robert Halford, Glenn Tipton & Alan Atkins

Intro

riff 1

E	D	B	B♭	A	G	F♯	E		E	E♭	D	B	B♭	A	G	F♯
9fr	7fr	9fr	8fr	7fr	10fr	9fr	7fr		7fr	6fr	5fr	7fr	6fr	5fr	3fr	2fr
③	③	④	④	④	⑤	⑤	⑤		⑤	⑤	⑤	⑥	⑥	⑥	⑥	⑥

riff 2

‖: **D5 E5 D5 E5** | **E5 D5** (B B♭ A G, 7fr 6fr 5fr 3fr, ⑥⑥⑥⑥) | **D5 E5 D5 E5** | **E5 D5** (B B♭ A G, 7fr 6fr 5fr 3fr, ⑥⑥⑥⑥) :‖

| **A5** | | **C5** | (**C5**) | **D5** | | **A5** | | **C5** | **G5** |

| **D5 E5 D5 E5** | **E5 D5** (B B♭ A G, 7fr 6fr 5fr 3fr, ⑥⑥⑥⑥) | **D5 E5 D5 E5** | **E5 D5** (B B♭ A G, 7fr 6fr 5fr 3fr, ⑥⑥⑥⑥) |

| riff 1 | (riff 1) ‖

Verse 1

E5
Whiskey woman don't you know

That you are drivin' me insane

E5
The liquor you give stems your will to live

E5w/riff 2
and gets right to my brain

Don't you know you're driving me insane?
A5   **C5**   **D5**
You're tryin' to find your way through life
A5   **C5** **G5** **E5w/riff 2**
You're tryin' to get some new —— di - rection
A5   **C5** **D5**
Another woman's got her man
A5   **C5** **G5** **E5w/riff 2**
But she won't find no new —— con - nection
B5
Takes another drink or two,
       C5 **B5** (**E5w/riff 2**)
Things look better when she's through.

Link 1 | D5 E5   D5 E5 | E5 D5 ♪ ♪ ♪ ♪ | D5 E5 E5 D5 | (D5) | N.C. ‖

B   B♭   A   G
7fr 6fr 5fr 3fr
⑥   ⑥   ⑥   ⑥

| E5 | E5 | A5 | A5 |

| D5 | D5 | A5 | B5 |

| N.C.(E5) | (E5) | (E5) | (E5) ‖

Verse 2

E5   E5w/riff 2
Takes another look around, you're not goin' anywhere

E5   E5w/riff 2
You've realized you're gettin' old and no one seems to care

A5   C5   D5
   You're tryin' to find your way again

A5   C5   G5   E5w/riff 2
   You're tryin' to find some new.——

A5   C5   D5
   Another woman's got her man

A5   C5   G5   E5w/riff 2
   But she won't find a new——

B5
Takes another drink or two,

                    C5   B5   (E5w/riff 2)
Things look better when she's through.

B   B♭   A   G
7fr 6fr 5fr 3fr
⑥   ⑥   ⑥   ⑥

Link 2 | D5 E5   D5 E5 | E5 D5 ♪ ♪ ♪ ♪ | D5 E5 E5 A5 | (A5) | N.C. ‖

Bridge

*A5   G5   F♯5   G5   C5
You 'bin foolin' with some hot guy

A5   G5   F♯5   G5   C5
I want to know why is it   why

E5   D5   C♯5   D5   G5
Get up, get out you know you really blew it

    E5   D5   C♯5   D5 G5
I've had enough, I've had enough, good God——— pluck me.

*(*Play lowest single note of chord only)*

Solo ‖: E5 | D5 | C♯5 | D5 G5 :‖

Play 8 times

‖: E5 | E5 | E5 | E5 :‖

| E5   A5 | F♯5 | C5   G5 | (G5) C5 D5 | D5 A5 B5⌢ |

‖: E5 | D5 | E5 | G5   D5 :‖ *Play 4 times*

(4°) Once she was...

180

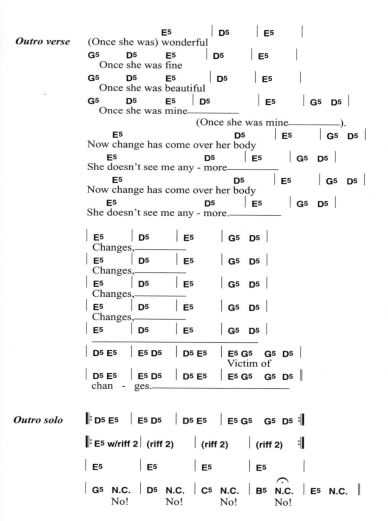

Outro verse

| | E5 | | D5 | | E5 | |
(Once she was) wonderful

| G5 | D5 | E5 | | D5 | | E5 | |
Once she was fine

| G5 | D5 | E5 | | D5 | | E5 | |
Once she was beautiful

| G5 | D5 | E5 | D5 | | E5 | G5 D5 |
Once she was mine_____
(Once she was mine_____).

| E5 | | D5 | E5 | G5 D5 |
Now change has come over her body

| E5 | | D5 | E5 | G5 D5 |
She doesn't see me any - more_____

| E5 | | D5 | E5 | G5 D5 |
Now change has come over her body

| E5 | | D5 | E5 | G5 D5 |
She doesn't see me any - more._____

| E5 | D5 | E5 | G5 D5 |
Changes,_____

| E5 | D5 | E5 | G5 D5 |
Changes,_____

| E5 | D5 | E5 | G5 D5 |
Changes,_____

| E5 | D5 | E5 | G5 D5 |
Changes,_____

| E5 | D5 | E5 | G5 D5 |

| D5 E5 | E5 D5 | D5 E5 | E5 G5 G5 D5 |
Victim of

| D5 E5 | E5 D5 | D5 E5 | E5 G5 G5 D5 ‖
chan - ges._____

Outro solo

‖: D5 E5 | E5 D5 | D5 E5 | E5 G5 G5 D5 :‖

‖: E5 w/riff 2 | (riff 2) | (riff 2) | (riff 2) :‖

| E5 | E5 | E5 | E5 |

| G5 N.C. | D5 N.C. | C5 N.C. | B5 N.C. | E5 N.C. ‖
No!   No!   No!   No!

181

Wake Up

Words by Zack De La Rocha
Music by Rage Against The Machine

Tune Guitar: D A D G B E

Intro

D(♭5)	(D(♭5))	D5	(D5)	
D(♭5)	(D(♭5))	D5	(D5)	
D5	(D5)	Cmaj9/D	(Cmaj9/D)
D5	(D5)	N.C.	N.C.

Come on!

riff 1

| (D5) | (D5) | (D5) | |
| (D5) | | N.C. (D5) |

riff 2

Verse 1   Come on, although ya try to dis - credit

Ya still never read it

w/riff 2
The needle, I'll thread it

Radically poetic

w/riff 2
Standin' with the fury that they had in '66

w/riff 2

cont.   And like E-Double I'm mad

Still knee-deep in the system's shit

w/riff 2
Hoover, he was a body remover

    w/riff 2
I'll give ya a dose

But it can never come close

     w/riff 2
To the rage built up inside of me

w/riff 2 N.C.
Fist in the air, in the land of hypocrisy.

w/riff 2

Verse 2   Movements come and movements go

w/riff 2
Leaders speak, movements cease

When their heads are flown

w/riff 2
'Cause all these punks

Got bullets in their heads

    D7♯9
De - partments of police, the judges, the feds.

w/riff 2
Networks at work, keepin' people calm

     w/riff 2
You know they went after King

When he spoke out on Vietnam

w/riff 2
  He turned the power to the have-nots

w/riff 2 N.C.
  And then came the shot.

Link 1

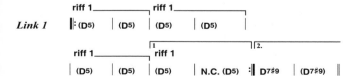

183

riff 3_____
C D   F F G   G   G Ab   F F G C
3fr 5fr 3fr 3fr 5fr 5fr 5fr 6fr 3fr 3fr 5fr 3fr
⑤ ⑤   ④ ④ ④   ④   ④ ④   ④ ④ ④ ⑤

w/riff 2

Verse 3   Wit' poetry, my mind I flex

      w/riff 2
Flip like Wilson, vocals never lackin' dat finesse

w/riff 2
Whadda I got to, whadda I got to do to wake ya up

    w/riff 3
To shake ya up, to break the structure up

     w/riff 2
'Cause blood still flows in the gutter

       w/riff 2
I'm like takin' photos

Mad boy kicks open the shutter

w/riff 2
Set the groove

Then stick and move like I was Cassius

w/riff 2   N.C.
Rep the stutter step

Then bomb a left upon the fascists.

w/riff 2

Verse 4   Yea, the several federal men

      w/riff 2
Who pulled schemes on the dream

And put it to an end

   w/riff 2
Ya better beware

Of retribution with mind war

D7(5)   **D7(♭5)**
20/20 visions and murals with metaphors

w/riff 2
Networks at work, keepin' people calm

     w/riff 2
Ya know they murdered X

184

cont. And tried to blame it on Islam

w/riff 2
　He turned the power to the have-nots

w/riff 2 N.C.
And then came the shot.

Middle

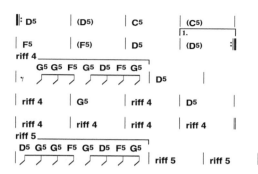

| ‖: D5 | (D5) | C5 | (C5) |
| F5 | (F5) | D5 | (D5) :‖ |

riff 4 _____
G5 G5 F5 G5 D5 F5 G5

| riff 4 | G5 | riff 4 | D5 |
| riff 4 | riff 4 | riff 4 | riff 4 ‖ |

riff 5 _____
D5 G5 G5 F5 G5 D5 F5 G5

| riff 5 | riff 5 |

Bridge

w/riff 5 *(x4)*
What was the price on his head?

w/riff 5　　　　　　**D5**
What was the price on his head!

(D5)
I think I heard a shot

I think I heard a shot

I think I heard a shot

riff 6 _____

| D(♭5) | (D(♭5)) | D5 | (D5) |
| D(♭5) | (D(♭5)) | D5 | (D5) |

I think I heard a shot

　　　　　　w/riff 6
I think I heard a shot

I think I heard,

　　　N.C.
I think I heard a shot.

| (D5) | (D5) | (D5) | (D5) |

Verse 5

D5   **Cmaj9/D**
He may be a real contender for this position should he
      D5
abandon his supposed obedience to white liberal doctrine
      Cmaj9/D
of non-violence... and embrace black nationalism'
D5   **Cmaj9/D**
  'Through counter-intelligence it should be possible to
                   D5
pinpoint potential trouble-makers... and neutralize them.
                 Cmaj9/D
Through counter-intelligence it should be possible to
               D5
pinpoint potential trouble-makers...   and neutralize them
    N.C.
and neutralize them, and neutralize them, and neutralize them.'

Outro

w/riff 1 (*x3*)   **D5**
Wake up! Wake up! Wake up! Wake up!
w/riff 1 (*x4*)   **w/riff 1** (*ad lib.*)
Wake up! Wake up! Wake up! Wake up!
N.C.(D5)   **N.C.**
How long? Not long, cause what you reap is what you sow

Walk This Way

Words & Music by
Joe Perry & Steven Tyler

Intro

| 2 |

┌─────── **Riff** ───────────────────┐
A B♭ B E A B♭ B E E │ A B♭ B E A B♭ B E G E │

── **(Riff)** ─────────────────────────┐
│ A B♭ B E A B♭ B E E │ A B♭ B E A B♭ B E A5 ‖

Verse 1

C7
Backstroke lover always hidin' 'neath the cover,

Still I talked to your daddy he say,

He said you ain't seen nothing 'til you're down on a muffin,

Then you're sure to be a-changin' your ways.

I met a cheerleader, was a real young bleeder,

All the times I can reminisce,

'Cause the best thing lovin'

With her sister and her cousin

Only started with a little kiss, like this!

Link 1

| **Riff** | **(Riff)** | **(Riff)** | **(Riff)** ‖

Verse 2

C7
See-saw swingin' with the boys in the school

And your feet flyin' up in the air,

Singin' hey diddle-diddle with the kitty in the middle,

You be swingin' like you just didn't care.

C⁷

cont. So I took a big chance at the high school dance

With a missy who was ready to play

Was it me she was foolin'

'Cause she knew what she was doin'

And I know love was here to stay

When she told me to

C¹³   **F**⁷
Chorus 1 Walk this way, walk this way
C¹³   **F**⁷
Walk this way, walk this way
C¹³   **F**⁷
Walk this way, walk this way
C¹³   **F**⁷
Walk this way, walk this way
                C⁷ | **C**⁷ | **C**⁷ | **C**⁷
Ah, just give me a kiss
          A⁵
- like this!

Link 2 | **Riff** | **(Riff)** | **(Riff)** | **(Riff)** ‖

C⁷
Verse 3 School girl Sadie with the classy, kinda sassy,

Little skirt climbing way up her knees,

There was three young ladies in the school gym locker

When I noticed they was lookin' at me.

I was a high school loser

Never made it with a lady

Till the boys told me something I missed,

Then my next door neighbour

cont.	With a daughter had a favour,
	C7
	So I gave her just a little kiss, like this!

Link 3 | Riff | (Riff) | (Riff) | (Riff) ‖

C7

Verse 4 See-saw swingin' with the boys in the school

And your feet flyin' up in the air ,

Singin' hey diddle-diddle with the kitty in the middle,

You be swingin' like you just didn't care.

So I took a big chance at the high school dance

With a missy who was ready to play.

Was it me she was foolin',

'Cause she knew what she was doin',

When she told me how to walk this way.

She told me to

C13   **F7**

Chorus 2 Walk this way, walk this way,

C13   **F7**

Walk this way, walk this way,

C13   **F7**

Walk this way, walk this way ,

C13   **F7**

Walk this way, walk this way,

                      C7 | **C7** | **C7** | **C7**

Ah, just give me a kiss

               A5

       - like this!

Outro ‖: Riff | (Riff) | (Riff) | (Riff) :‖ *Repeat to fade*

(Guitar solo)

War Pigs

Words & Music by
Terence Butler, John Osbourne, Frank Iommi & William Ward

Intro

‖: E5 | E5 | D5 | D5 :‖
Play 3 times

| E5 | D5 | E5 | D5 |

| D5 E5 N.C | N.C | D5 E5 | N.C ‖

Verse 1

D5 E5 N.C
　　Generals gathered in their masses,
D5 E5 N.C
　　Just like witches at black masses.
D5 E5 N.C
　　Evil minds that plot destruction,
D5 E5 N.C
　　Sorcerer of death's construction.
D5 E5 N.C
　　In the fields the bodies burning,
D5 E5 N.C
　　As the war machine keeps turning.
D5 E5 N.C
　　Death and hatred to mankind,
D5 E5 N.C
　　Poisoning their brainwashed minds.

　　Oh Lord yeah!

Link 1

‖: D5 E5 G5 F#5 | F5 E5 :‖ *Play 4 times*

| E5 G5 | E5 G5 | E5 G5 | E5 G5 ‖

	E5
Bridge 1	Politicians hide themselves away,

They only started the war.

Why should they go out to fight,

They leave that role to the poor.

Yeah!

Link 2 | E5 G5| E5 G5| E5 G5| E5 G5‖

E5

Bridge 2 Time will tell on their power minds,

Making war just for fun.

Treating people just like pawns in chess,

Wait 'till their judgement day comes.

Yeah!

Link 3 ‖: D5 E5 G5 F#5 | F5 E5 :‖ *Play 4 times*

Solo ‖: E5 :‖ *Play 18 times*

| E5 | D5 | E5 | D5 |

|D5 E5 N.C| N.C | D5 E5 N.C | D5 E5 N.C ‖

D5 E5 N.C

Verse 1   Now in darkness, world stops turning,

D5 E5 N.C

Ashes where the bodies burning.

D5 E5 N.C

No more war pigs have the power,

D5 E5 N.C

Hand of God has struck the hour.

D5 E5 N.C

Day of judgement, God is calling,

D5 E5 N.C

On their knees, the war pigs crawling.

D5 E5 N.C

Begging mercy for their sins,

D5 E5 N.C

Satan laughing, spreads his wings.

Oh Lord yeah!

Link 4   As link 3

Outro | Em7   ‖: Em7 | E5 B5 D5 | Em7 | E5 G5 E5 :‖

‖: Em7 | Em7 :‖ Dm7 | Dm7 | Cm7 | Cm7 |

| B5 C5 | B5 ‖: E5 | D5   :‖ *Play 24 times*

| Em7 | Em7 | Em7 D5 | E5   ‖